C Programming for Electronic Engineers

Other titles of related interest

B.W. Allen, *Analogue Electronics for Higher Studies*
W.A. Atherton, *From Compass to Computer*
J.C. Cluley, *Transistors for Microprocessor Systems*
Donard de Cogan, *Solid State Devices - A Quantum Physics Approach*
C.W. Davidson, *Transmission Lines for Communications, second edition*
M.E. Goodge, *Analog Electronics*
B.A. Gregory, *An Introduction to Electrical Instrumentation and Measurement
    Systems, second edition*
Paul A. Lynn, *An Introduction to the Analysis and Processing of Signals, third
    edition*
R.J. Mitchell, *Microprocessor Systems – An Introduction*
Noel M. Morris, *Electrical Circuit Analysis and Design*
Mark S. Nixon, *Introductory Digital Design – A Programmable Approach*
R.G. Powell, *Electromagnetism*
P. Silvester, *Electric Circuits*
M.J. Usher and D.A. Keating, *Sensors and Transducers, second edition*
L.A.A. Warnes, *Electronic and Electrical Engineering – Principles and Practice*
L.A.A. Warnes, *Electronic Materials*
B.W. Williams, *Power Electronics – Devices, Drivers, Applications and Passive
    Components*

New Electronics Series

G.J. Awcock and R.Thomas, *Applied Image Processing*
Rodney F.W. Coates, *Underwater Acoustic Systems*
M.D. Edwards, *Automatic Logic Synthesis Techniques for Digital Systems*
Peter J. Fish, *Electronic Noise and Low Noise Design*
W. Forsythe and R.M. Goodall, *Digital Control*
C.G. Guy, *Data Communications for Engineers*
Paul A. Lynn, *Digital Signals, Processors and Noise*
Paul A. Lynn, *Radar Systems*
R.C.V. Macario, *Cellular Radio - Principles and Design*
A.F. Murray and H.M. Reekie, *Integrated Circuit Design*
F.J. Owens, *Signal Processing of Speech*
Dennis N. Pim, *Television and Teletext*
M. Richharia, *Satellite Communications Systems*
M.J.N. Sibley, *Optical Communications, second edition*
P.M. Taylor, *Robotic Control*
G.S. Virk, *Digital Computer Control Systems*
Allan Waters, *Active Filter Design*

C Programming
for Electronic Engineers

Keith Jackson BSc CEng MIEE

with acknowledgement to Gavin Earnshaw MEng

School of Electronic, Communication
and Electrical Engineering
University of Plymouth

MACMILLAN

First published 1995 by
MACMILLAN PRESS LTD
Houndmills, Basingstoke, Hampshire RG21 6XS
and London
Companies and representatives
throughout the world

ISBN 0-333-63780-1

A catalogue record for this book is available
from the British Library.

10   9   8   7   6   5   4   3   2   1
04   03   02   01   00   99   98   97   96   95

Printed in Great Britain by Antony Rowe Ltd, Chippenham, Wiltshire

To my parents, Ron and Joan.

Contents

Preface

This book is the product of many years of experience of teaching programming skills at tertiary, further and higher education colleges using a variety of languages. During this time it has been felt that text books available are usually unsuitable for Engineering students and so this book is an attempt to fill the gap.

Most texts available for students tend to be of the 'teach yourself' variety which, to a large extent, are slow and laborious to somebody who is following a computing course, or they are aimed at computer scientists who have considerably more time to learn programming skills than engineering students. Such books also tend to be bewilderingly comprehensive, large and expensive.

This book is designed for an engineering student who will probably have little time to learn programming but who will probably be expected to produce large and complex pieces of software during their college and subsequent careers. This book is therefore intended as a reference to complement a taught course in C programming. Given the pressures and time available to such students this book should allow them to quickly become competent in basic programming skills. This is not a comprehensive guide to C programming and some short cuts have been made which might upset the purist. We make no apologies for this since it is done in the interests of clarity and to avoid bogging the student down in detail.

The text includes aspects specifically of interest to electronic engineers including low-level operations, control and use of peripheral devices, graphics, electrical circuit calculations and exercises on simulation and numerical analysis. Coverage of issues such as program design methods and software engineering are not comprehensive since we believe that this is perhaps best left to the preference and style preferred by the lecturer in charge.

A number of pedagogic features are included such as quick self assessment tests at key points and chapter summaries. Complete case studies are also included and most chapters end with a few carefully selected exercises to reinforce the topics covered. Also included are numerous notes on the peculiarities often encountered by beginners using C. In our experience C is not a language for novices, but its wide acceptance in Electronics has forced its adoption on many courses as the only taught programming language. Included is an guide on fixing errors commonly encountered by students to make the experience a little less frustrating.

I hope the student finds this book of use during their first experience of programming and helps to set the foundations for further study. My thanks go to my colleagues at Plymouth for their inspiration.

Keith Jackson. Plymouth, April 1995.   E-mail jjackson@plymouth.ac.uk

1 Fundamentals

1.1 Introduction

In this chapter we will briefly examine the origins of C and look at its relative advantages and disadvantages. We will also introduce some basic arithmetical concepts with which any C programmer will need to be familiar.

1.2 Origins of C

The C language was first developed in the early 1970s in California, mainly for the development of operating systems. It was derived from earlier languages from which it inherited many of its features (its immediate predecessor was not surprisingly called 'B'). The language found applications in many areas and soon gained widespread use. This success then produced problems because many slightly different implementations of the language began to appear which made the portability of programs a problem. Therefore, the American National Standards Institute (ANSI) defined a standard to which most implementations now work. However, this has not halted the development of the language and new derivatives of the language have appeared; some, such as C++, are now in widespread use. Most of the programs in this book are written to the ANSI standard, but where this is not the case a note has been made.

1.3 Advantages and disadvantages of C

Like all other programming languages, C offers the programmer certain advantages and disadvantages. The advantages include widespread availability and portability which are due to the popularity of C in many disciplines and in many countries across the world. This is also helped by the standardisation of C which ensures that programs can be transferred across systems and still be used. This contrasts with languages such as BASIC, which has hundreds of implementations, but often BASIC programs cannot be transferred between systems due to a lack of standardisation (i.e. they use different keywords, syntax, etc.). Another useful feature of C is that it adopts a modular approach, meaning that a final program can be produced from several separate files containing C code. This allows several programmers to work on the same project and splits the program into manageable units. This contrasts with Pascal which expects the whole program to be contained in a single file.

From an engineer's point of view an important advantage of C is that it allows close interaction with the hardware, whereas other programming languages attempt to hide what goes on beneath the programmer's view of the system as much as possible. Consequently, C is more suitable for control-type applications where interaction with various external equipment and hardware is required.

On the negative side it should be noted that C is not really a beginner's language. Traditionally, languages such as Pascal which were designed specifically for teaching purposes were favoured for beginners. However, due to the widespread use of C, especially in engineering, many people now find that C is their first language. In principle C is no more complex than comparable languages such as Pascal or Modula-2, but unfortunately there is much more that can go wrong and confuse the novice. For reasons of efficiency C lacks much of the automatic checking available in other languages (such as detecting arithmetic overflows), which means that as the program runs things may go wrong and remain undetected until the user sees odd results being produced. Also, the syntax of C allows a small typing error to change change the meaning of a statement whilst still being valid. Therefore, no errors are detected, but the program does not behave as expected. To help the reader many of the more common errors and odd effects which occur are listed in appendix C.

1.4 Binary numbers

A fundamental concept of computing is the use of binary (base 2) numbers. This arises from the digital nature of computer hardware in which a signal can only have one of two states, for which the notation 1 and 0 is used. A group of signals can then be used to represent a more complex item of data such as a number. Note that the machine does not understand the concept of 'a number', but is simply a device for manipulating patterns of binary digits used to represent a number. To understand how a number can be represented in binary we must consider number bases.

The reader will be very familiar with base ten (decimal) numbers such as we use daily. Each digit of a number represents a multiple of ascending powers of ten (i.e. 1, 10, 100, 1000, etc.). For example, 23045 can be broken down as follows:

```
2 × 10⁴ = 20000
3 × 10³ =  3000
0 × 10² =   000
4 × 10¹ =    40
5 × 10⁰ =     5+
          _____
          23045
```

In binary arithmetic the same rule applies, but each digit position from the right represents ascending powers of 2 (i.e. 1, 2, 4, 8, 16, etc.). Also, each digit only has two possible values, instead of ten as in decimal. Therefore, the binary value 100110 may be converted to its decimal equivalent as follows:

```
1 × 2⁵ = 1 × 32 = 32
0 × 2⁴ = 0 × 16 =  0
0 × 2³ = 0 ×  8 =  0
1 × 2² = 1 ×  4 =  4
1 × 2¹ = 1 ×  2 =  2
0 × 2⁰ = 0 ×  1 =  0+
                  ──
                  38
```

Therefore, 1001100 is the binary representation of the decimal number 38. We can therefore convert any binary to decimal using the process above. To convert decimal numbers to binary is slightly more complex. The process basically involves dividing the decimal number by descending powers of two and each time keeping the remainder. For example, to convert 46 to binary we first choose the highest power of two which is less than or equal to 46. Given that the sequence of powers of two is 1, 2, 4, 8, 16, 32, 64, 128... then the largest of these by which 46 can be divided is 32. Therefore:

$$46 \div 2^5 = 46 \div 32 = 1 \text{ remainder } 14$$

We now divide the remainder by the next power of two down:

$$14 \div 2^4 = 14 \div 16 = 0 \text{ remainder } 14$$

This process continues down to division by 2^0. Hence overall we get:

```
46 ÷ 2⁵ = 46 ÷ 32 = 1 remainder 14
14 ÷ 2⁴ = 14 ÷ 16 = 0 remainder 14
14 ÷ 2³ = 14 ÷  8 = 1 remainder 6
 6 ÷ 2² =  6 ÷  4 = 1 remainder 2
 2 ÷ 2¹ =  2 ÷  2 = 1 remainder 0
 0 ÷ 2⁰ =  0 ÷  1 = 0 remainder 0
```

At the end of this process the remainder should be zero. The binary representation is now simply read down the column of the results of the divisions, which in this case is 101110.

The ability to convert binary numbers to decimal numbers and vice versa are not essential skills for a programmer but an understanding of these processes and a 'feel' for binary numbers can lead to a much better insight into how computers work and how programs behave.

1.5 Self-assessment test — Binary

Convert the following binary numbers to decimal:

a) 110010   b) 101010   c) 11110011

Convert the following decimal numbers to binary:

d) 54   e) 101   f) 252

Answers: a) 50 b) 42 c) 243 d) 110110 e) 1100101 f) 11111100

1.6 Binary arithmetic

Almost all programs contain some arithmetic operations, such as add or divide, and many contain more complex mathematical functions, such as calculating logarithms or sines of angles. However, the basic mechanism for calculating all of these depends on what sort of functions we can perform on binary values using the logic gates of which computers are composed. The basic operation from which most other arithmetic operations are derived is addition. The rules for the addition of two binary digits are as follows:

```
0 + 0 = 0
0 + 1 = 1
1 + 0 = 1
1 + 1 = 0 carry 1
```

The last case is the most interesting. In decimal terms this is 1 plus 1 gives 2 which in binary is represented as 10. Therefore, this has resulted in a carry to the next column, just as the addition of 4 and 6 does in decimal arithmetic. Therefore, to add two binary numbers of more than one digit we simply apply the rules above. For example, let us add the values 1101100 and 101101:

```
1101100
0101101+
‾‾‾‾‾‾‾
```

Working from the right, just as we do in decimal addition, the first column 0+1 gives 1, and the second column 0+0 gives 0:

```
1101100
0101101+
‾‾‾‾‾‾‾
     01
```

The next column is $1+1$ which gives 0 and a carry to the next column:

```
1101100
0101101+
```
```
 ¹001
```

This fourth column is now $1+1$ which gives 0 carry 1 plus the previous carry, so the result of this column is 1 carry 1 (i.e. $1+1+1$ gives 1 carry 1):

```
1101100
0101101+
```
```
 ¹1001
```

Completing the sum is this manner we obtain:

```
1101100
0101101+
```
```
10011001
```

To perform such additions in hardware it should be noted that the addition of two values can be performed using an exclusive-OR gate which has the truth table:

A	B	Z
0	0	0
0	1	1
1	0	1
1	1	0

where A and B are inputs and Z is the output. Also, the carry signal can be created using an AND gate which has the following truth table:

A	B	Z
0	0	0
0	1	0
1	0	0
1	1	1

This leads to the half adder circuit shown in Figure 1.1 which adds two binary digits. In order to add binary numbers of more than one digit we need a slightly more complex unit called a full adder which also adds the carry from the previous column. The full adder can then be used as the basis of a complete adder circuit which will quickly add together two multidigit binary numbers.

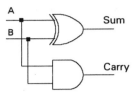

Figure 1.1 Half adder

Other arithmetic operations are based on the use of addition. For instance, to perform subtraction we can negate (make negative) one value and then add it to another using an adder unit. We will look at how we represent negative numbers in later chapters. To perform multiplication we can perform multiple additions and to perform division we can perform multiple subtractions. It is usual to have specialised circuits to perform multiplication and division as efficiently as possible, but these still usually incorporate the basic adder circuit. Therefore, we have the full range of basic arithmetic operations available.

One other simple operation often used is to shift a binary number left or right. Take the binary number 110011 which is decimal 51. If we shift it left by inserting an extra 0 we get 1100110 which is decimal 102. Therefore we have doubled the value. If we shift the number right by removing the last digit then 110011 becomes 11001 which is decimal 25. Therefore, we have halved the value and the digit removed represents the remainder, in this case 1.

Again, it should be noted that a programmer does not need to know about how arithmetic is performed, but an understanding of the principles does give a better insight into what is going on and also allows the programming of useful tricks when dealing with the low-level manipulation of data which we will examine much later.

1.7 Hexadecimal notation

We have so far represented binary numbers in terms of 1's and 0's. It is often useful to work in terms of binary notation, but this can become cumbersome since the numbers quickly become very long (e.g. ten digits are required to represent the binary value for one thousand). This has led to the creation of notations which are more manageable, but it still allows the user to quickly revert back to the binary pattern. This is achieved by giving symbols to all possible patterns for a small group of binary digits. The hexadecimal notation (often referred to as hex) works with groups of 4 binary digits of which there are sixteen combinations of 1's and 0's. These are assigned symbols (hex codes) as follows:

Binary	Hex Code	Decimal Value
0000	0	0
0001	1	1
0010	2	2
0011	3	3
0100	4	4
0101	5	5
0110	6	6
0111	7	7
1000	8	8
1001	9	9
1010	A	10
1011	B	11
1100	C	12
1101	D	13
1110	E	14
1111	F	15

Note that the hex notation resorts to using the letters A to F to make up the required 16 digits. Therefore, the binary number 1101 can be written in hex as simply 'D' and the number 11010011 can be written as 'D3'. To convert hexadecimal numbers to decimal is simple. The hex value 'B' is simply 11 in decimal from the table. If there is more than one hex digit then each extra digit has sixteen times the weight of the previous one. For example, the hex value 'E4' can be converted to decimal as follows:

```
4 (hex)  = 4  (decimal)         = 4
E (hex)  = 14 (decimal) × 16 = 224+

                               ────
                               228
```

Similarly, the hex value 'F3A5' in decimal is:

```
5 (hex)  =  5 (decimal) × 16⁰ = 5
A (hex)  = 10 (decimal) × 16¹ = 160
3 (hex)  =  3 (decimal) × 16² = 768
F (hex)  = 15 (decimal) × 16³ = 61440+

                               ─────
                               62373
```

To convert a decimal number to hex, keep dividing it by sixteen and note the remainders. For example, to convert 34567 to hex we proceed as follows:

```
34667 ÷ 16 = 2166 remainder 11 (B in Hex)
 2166 ÷ 16 = 135  remainder 6  (6 in Hex)
  135 ÷ 16 = 8    remainder 7  (7 in Hex)
    8 ÷ 16 = 0    remainder 8  (8 in Hex)
```

The final answer is obtained by reading off the remainders in hex upwards to obtain '876B'.

1.8 Octal notation

The hexadecimal notation is basically a base 16 number system which conveniently ties up with binary, since four binary digits have 16 combinations. We can, if we choose, code up groups of three digits of which there are eight combinations. This leads to a notation called octal which is essentially a base eight number system. The coding used to represent three binary digits is as follows:

Binary	Octal Code	Decimal Value
000	0	0
001	1	1
010	2	2
011	3	3
100	4	4
101	5	5
110	6	6
111	7	7

In this case the first seven decimal digits are used. Beware as this means that octal values appear indistinguishable from decimal values! The means of converting binary and decimal values to octal and vice versa is exactly the same as for hex, but use the value 8 in the processes instead of 16.

1.9 Self-assessment test − Number bases

Attempt these problems using the techniques described above. Many calculators will do these conversions directly, but using one will not help the reader gain an insight into the processes involved, so it is better to try them manually.

Add together the following binary numbers:

a)   1001+1011 b)   11101+101010   c)   1111101+100

Convert the following binary numbers to decimal:

d) 1101 e) 11001100   f) 10000

Convert the following decimal numbers to binary:

g) 23   h) 1024   i) 750

Convert the following decimal numbers to hexadecimal:

j) 45   k) 1024   l) 65535

Convert the following hexadecimal numbers to decimal:

m) 4E   n) 6A7F   o) FF

Convert the following octal numbers to decimal:

p) 34   q) 10   r) 567

Convert the following decimal numbers to octal:

s) 55   t) 64   u) 80

Answers: a) 10100   b) 1000111   c) 10000001 d) 13   e) 204   f) 16   g) 10111
h) 10000000000 i) 1011101110 j) 2D k) 400   l) FFFF   m) 78   n) 27263
o) 255 p) 28 q) 8   r) 375   s) 67 t) 100 u) 120

1.10   Summary

- Values are stored and processed by a computer in binary format (i.e. as sequences of 1's and 0's).

- Addition can be performed on two binary numbers using simple logic gates. This forms the basis of all other common arithmetic operations.

- Hexadecimal is the base sixteen number system. It is useful because it is easy to convert hexadecimal numbers directly into binary. The characters A to E are used to make up the required number of digits.

- Octal is the base eight number system and has similar advantages to hexadecimal. However, its use is increasingly uncommon.

2 Programming Concepts

2.1 Introduction

In this chapter we will explain the basic concepts of writing high-level computer programs. It is important that a programmer understands the processes that need to take place to ensure that a finished program can be run. This will allow him to deal with errors more effectively and also to appreciate the logic behind the structure of the C language. We will start with a very brief look at how a typical computer is constructed and how it operates, which will lead us on to examining the necessity for high-level programming languages such as C. We will also examine the general structure and layout of a C program.

2.2 Computer hardware

There are thousands of makes and models of computer but the majority are very similar in their structure and operation. A typical and simple system (such as the average personal computer) is shown in Figure 2.1.

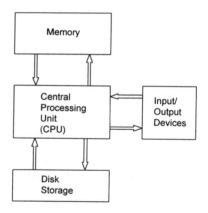

Figure 2.1 Simple computer system

The heart of the system is the central processing unit (CPU) which is in effect the 'brain' of the machine and is responsible for processing data and coordinating movement of information between itself and the other components of the system. The CPU works under the control of a program (i.e. a set of instructions) which may be very complex to cover all eventualities.

A program which is being executed resides in the block marked 'memory'. The memory of a computer is a vast array (many millions) of transistor circuits which can be turned on or off to represent a binary digit (1 or 0). A binary digit is usually referred to as a 'bit'. Programs and data are therefore represented in memory as a sequence of bits using a code which can be interpreted by the CPU. The CPU can very quickly access instructions and data from the memory as it advances through its program and can typically execute millions of instructions every second.

The memory has some severe drawbacks. Because it is essentially a collection of electronic switches, any removal of power to the machine means that the contents of the memory is lost, thus making it unsuitable for storing programs and data permanently. Also, the size of the memory is not large enough to store the numerous programs which might be required on a typical system. Consequently, we need a mass storage facility from which we can load up the memory with any program we wish to run. The solution to this problem is to use magnetic disk units for permanent mass storage. These devices are not volatile (i.e. do not 'forget' when power is removed) and can store many thousands of millions of bits. However, they cannot replace the memory since they are slow when the CPU needs to access information (thousands of times slower than memory).

The information on a disk is generally organised into units called files. A file is essentially an area of disk which can contain a program or some data. The 'C' programs that you will write will each be contained in file to which you will assign a name, so that you can access it later. You will need to become familiar with the organisation of files on the system that you will be using.

A computer needs some means of interacting with the outside world and so it will have input and output devices. Typical input devices include keyboards, mice, communication links or interfaces to physical measurement devices such as temperature probes and switches. The CPU can access any data supplied by these devices when necessary. Output devices include video monitors, sound generators, printers or interfaces to control equipment such as a robot arm.

2.3 Operating systems

When initially switched on the CPU runs a program called the operating system. This keeps the machine 'ticking over' and allows the user to control the machine so that other programs (application programs) can be run. The operating system remains in overall control of the machine at all times and even if an application program should go badly wrong the operating system can take over, report problems and terminate the faulty program.

There are many different operating systems running on different machines and it will be desirable to find out the basic commands that the operating system to be used makes available to the user.

2.4 Memory structure

Computer memory is organised into a structure such that it can efficiently hold programs and information and such that the CPU can easily access any item in the memory. As already mentioned, the memory consists of millions of electronics circuits which can be in one of two states to represent a single bit. These bits are collected into groups of eight to form what is called a byte. With eight bits in a byte we can have 2^8 (or 256) combinations of 1's and 0's. This allows us to represent numbers from 0 to 255, or to represent characters by assigning a particular combination to particular character (e.g. the pattern 01000001 is usually used to represent the letter 'A'). If we need to represent larger numbers we can combine bytes to form groups of 16 or 32 bits (often referred to as words).

We also need a means of accessing a particular byte in memory and so we assign a number (called an address) to each byte starting from zero upwards. We

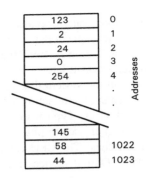

Figure 2.2 Memory structure

can therefore view memory as a large array of boxes, each with a unique address and containing a value between 0 and 255 as shown in Figure 2.2. This represents a small memory of 2^{10} bytes (1024 bytes or 1 kbyte).

The CPU reads data from memory simply by passing an address to the memory hardware. The memory then responds by passing back the data at that address within a few tens of nanoseconds (1 ns $= 10^{-9}$ s). Alternatively, the CPU may wish to store some data in memory and so provides an address and the byte to be stored in the memory. The memory hardware then replaces whatever was already in the specified address with the new value supplied by the CPU. The original contents of the memory location is therefore lost forever.

Many modern machines can read or write several bytes (a word) to memory in one operation.

2.5 Machine code

From the moment a computer is switched on, the CPU needs to be told what it should be doing and so there must be a program in memory for it to follow. Initially the operating system is loaded into memory from disk in a process called 'booting'. The operating system program then allows us to load other programs from the disk into memory and run them. These other programs might include word processors, spreadsheets or a C compiler, which we will discuss later.

In most machines the CPU consists of a single silicon chip called a microprocessor which contains circuitry for performing arithmetic, making decisions, storing data (registers), moving data and for controlling all these functions. The control circuitry is driven by the program being executed and so it must be able to interpret the program information stored in memory.

A program in memory is stored as a sequence of bytes. Each of the possible CPU operations is represented by a byte code or a sequence of byte codes. When running a program the CPU steps through a sequence of these instruction codes one after another. This type of program is called machine code simply because it is the form of program that the CPU understands. We will illustrate this concept with a simplified example.

The diagram in Figure 2.3 represents a simple CPU and its associated memory. The CPU consists of an arithmetic unit for performing simple arithmetic operations, two registers called A and B which are storage registers for bytes inside the CPU, a control unit for interpreting the program commands and a register called a program counter. The program counter contains the memory address of the instruction in memory being executed and is incremented when the instruction finishes so that it points to the next instruction to be executed. This is the means by which the CPU keeps track of its position in the program.

In the diagram we can see that the program counter contains the value 152, indicating that the code in memory location 152 represents the next program instruction. The CPU sends this address to the memory circuitry along a group of wires called an address bus. It also signals to the memory on a separate read/write wire that it wants to read this address. The memory responds by returning the value 56 on another group of wires called the data bus. The control unit now decodes this value to determine what to do next. Let us assume that 56 represents the following instruction:

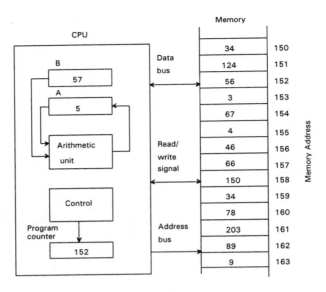

Figure 2.3 CPU and memory

"Load the value immediately following this
instruction in memory into register A."

The CPU therefore makes another read request to memory for the contents of location 153 and the data returned is placed in register 'A'. This results in the value 5 in 'A' being overwritten with 3. The program counter is then incremented by 2 so that it points to the next instruction in location 154. Let us assume that this code (67) represents the following instruction:

"Load the value immediately following this
instruction in memory into register B."

After this instruction we have 3 in 'A', 4 in 'B' and the program counter pointing at location 156. The next instruction (46) is interpreted by the CPU as:

"Add the contents of registers A and B and
place the result back into A."

This causes the contents of the two registers to be sent into the arithmetic unit which adds them together and places the result (7) back into register 'A'. The program counter is now incremented by one to point to the next instruction at location 157. Let us assume that the code 66 is interpreted as:

> ```
> "Store the contents of A at the memory
> location whose address follows this instruction"
> ```

This means that the CPU looks at the contents of the next location (158) and finds the value 150. It then stores the contents of register 'A' (7) at location 150 in memory.

A number of things should become apparent from this example. Firstly, machine code involves a lot of very simple tasks to perform any useful function. Fortunately, the machine can execute millions of these simple instructions each second and so can very effectively perform much more complex tasks even if it does mean doing the job in many simple steps. Secondly, machine code is not 'user friendly' and is difficult for humans to interpret. In the early days of computing all programming was done in machine code, but it is difficult to write, makes program production slow and it is prone to errors. The third point is a plus point for machine code. We can program the machine to do exactly what we want in precise detail, which makes the program very efficient and fast. Consequently, machine code is still used for critical sections of programs which must execute quickly.

2.6 High- and low-level languages

Anyone who has programmed in machine code will tell you that it is not simple, but the task can be made easier by using a software tool called an assembler. When writing programs using an assembler the programmer produces a file in which each machine instruction is represented by a mnemonic. Our previous machine code example might therefore become:

```
LOADA   3        (i.e. Load Register A with 3)
LOADB   4        (i.e. Load Register B with 4)
ADD              (i.e. Add B to A)
STOREA  150      (i.e. Store A at address 150)
```

The complete program file is then processed by the assembler which produces a second file containing the machine code. This is obviously much more user friendly but it is still a laborious and error-prone task when producing complex programs. Assembly code is termed a low-level language because each instruction entered by the programmer corresponds to one machine code instruction.

An improved situation is where we can write our instructions in a fashion more natural to humans, such as:

```
answer=3+4;
```

In this example we have effectively programmed the same task as before but this time using the C language. We can now use another software tool called a compiler which converts this to machine code. It can result in exactly the same machine code as before (where *answer* is a name for location 150 in memory). However, in this case we are not concerned with specific CPU instructions, we do not necessarily know (or care) where in memory *answer* is stored and we have produced several machine instructions in one statement.

This is an example of high-level language programming where a single high-level statement can produce tens or hundreds of machine code instructions when processed by a compiler. It means that our programs are smaller, easier to understand, easier to write and independent of the machine on which they are run, since we can use a compiler designed to produce machine code specific to the machine in use. This last point is important because different types of machine have different machine code sets. However, our programs can still run on any machine provided that we have a compiler appropriate to each type of machine. Therefore, high-level programs are said to be portable, since they make no assumptions about machine instructions, whereas low-level programming languages tend to be machine specific.

2.7 Compilers and linkers

It is important from an early stage that a programmer realises the role of compilers and linkers in producing a program. Program production starts with a programmer writing a program in a high-level language (such as C) which when completed resembles English statements. The program is then saved in a file on disk which is referred to as a source code file. Unfortunately, this program cannot be run directly on the machine because the CPU only understands machine code programs and not C programs. Therefore, we need a tool which will convert our 'human readable' C program to a 'machine readable' machine code program. The tool we use is called a compiler which in general is very easy to use. The compiler also performs other tasks, such as checking our C program for any obvious mistakes. The output of the compiler is called an object file which consists of 'nearly' ready-to-run machine code.

When programs are produced in high-level languages we often make use of prewritten sections of code to perform common tasks such as printing a message on the monitor or finding the square root of a number. These are called standard library functions and their use saves a lot of time and repetition for the programmer. Also, in large projects many people may be writing different sections of the program in separate files. We therefore need to bring all these individual contributions and library functions together when we produce the final machine code program. This is done using a software tool called a linker.

The individual object files produced by the compiler are not fixed at any particular place in memory. This means that any machine code instruction which refers to an item in memory may be incomplete as the address is not yet known. One of the linker's jobs is to decide where the code in each contributing object file is placed in the memory and then tie up any address references between them. The output of the linker is our final machine code program in a file called an executable file. The process is summarised in Figure 2.4.

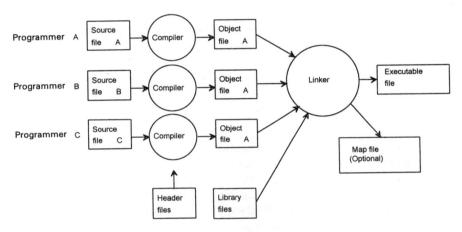

Figure 2.4 Program compilation and linking

Any library functions usually exist as precompiled object files (called library files) which the linker will automatically access when necessary. The compiler also needs some information about these functions which it accesses from files called header files.

Notice also the optional map file. This can be produced by the linker to tell the user at what memory addresses it has placed various items of data and code. This is sometimes useful for tracing errors.

The final stage in running a program is to load the executable file containing machine code from the disk to the machines memory and then to set the CPU running at the start address of the program. This is done by a program called a loader which is usually part of the operating system. This is usually an automatic process and not one which the novice programmer needs to worry about.

To create and edit the source files the programmer(s) can use readily available editor programs. However, many modern C development systems combine editor, compiler, linker and debugging facilities into a single consistent environment making the programmer's life much easier. This is something you will need to investigate on the system you use before you can begin programming.

2.8 Structure of a C program

We will now start to examine the layout of some simple C programs to illustrate how they are structured. Let us consider a very common program often used by even the most experienced programmers when they first start to learn a new language. The program simply writes on the monitor the message *"Hello World!"*. The code to do this is shown below

```
/* Simple program to write message on the screen */

#include <stdio.h>

main()
{
  printf("Hello World!");
}
```

The program starts with a comment. A comment is a piece of text between the symbols /* and */ but is not considered to form part of the program and is placed in the code so as to annotate it for future reference. Comments can be placed anywhere in a program and there is no restriction on their size or number. A good programmer will always properly comment his program so that others can understand how it works.

The next line starts with the word *#include*. This tells the compiler to include at this point the contents of a file into the program. The name of the file to be inserted is then given inside < > symbols and, in this case, it is a file called *stdio.h*. This type of file is called a header file and may be hundreds of lines long. When compiled the contents of the entire header file is 'pasted' into our program in place of the *#include* line.

The *stdio.h* header file contains sections of C code which our program requires in order to be able to perform any input and output operations. Although the program does not require any input it does perform output operations when writing a message to the monitor. The use of this header file is very convenient since we can write programs which perform input and output without having to worry too much about the information required by our program to perform these tasks. The precise nature of the contents of header files will become more apparent in later chapters.

The next line indicates the start of the main body of our program. This is indicated by the word *main()* followed the body of the program contained within curly braces *"{....}"*. This section of our program is referred to as the *main* function and every program must have this function within it. When the program is run it begins execution from the statement following the { symbol and then continues until it reaches the corresponding } symbol where the program ends. The program above only has a single statement inside the *main* function but there could be thousands.

A statement is an instruction which is executed when the program is run. In this case we have a single *printf* statement which is used to print messages on the monitor. The message we require to be printed follows the word *printf* inside brackets and double quotes. In fact what we are doing here is using a prewritten section of code called a function which is labelled *printf*. This function is specifically written to print messages onto the monitor. Since this is such a common task it saves a lot of time and effort if we can make use of this function. The actual code for *printf* resides in the library files and so it is referred to as a library function.

When this program is compiled, linked and run the result is the following message appearing on the monitor:

```
Hello World!
```

2.9 Generalised program layout

The program illustrated in the previous section is a very simple example. More complex programs will have additional sections which can be generalised in the framework shown in Figure 2.5. The precise order and layout of a program is flexible to some degree, but we will adopt a consistent layout which should minimise problems. Not all sections labelled have yet been covered but these will be described as we progress.

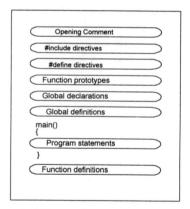

Figure 2.5 Generalised C program layout

C is a free format language. This means that there is a certain amount of flexibility concerning layout. For example, it is possible to have several statements on one line or one statement spaced over several lines. We will examine how best to lay out programs in later chapters.

2.10   Preprocessor

It is worth at this stage looking in a little more detail at the steps involved when a program is compiled. As we have already seen the program we write and the program which is compiled can be different because any *#include* lines result in the inclusion of whole files. There are also other ways in which our program may become changed before it is compiled. Compilation is therefore a two-stage process. The first stage involves preprocessing the original file with regard to preprocessor directives such as *#include*. The resulting file is then passed to the compiler for conversion to object files. Note that the preprocessor does not modify our original source file. Instead it takes a copy of the source file each time it is compiled and then works on the copy. This process is summarised in Figure 2.6.

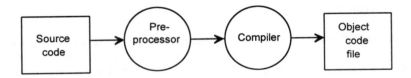

Figure 2.6 Compiler and preprocessor

The preprocessor is controlled by using preprocessor directives. These are indicated in our programs by single words prefixed with a hash (#). There are several directives listed below, some of which we will use in later chapters. At the moment the only one with which we are familiar is *#include*.

```
#include
#define
#if
#def
#ifdef
#enddef
```

Note the difference between a directive and a statement. A preprocessor directive affects the way in which the program is compiled, whereas a statement is a program instruction to be compiled (i.e. converted to machine code).

2.11   ANSI standard

There are many compilers produced for many machines by different software manufactures. It would make life very difficult for the programmer if each compiler used a slightly different version of the rules of the C language. It would also mean that programs would not be portable between different machines or compilers.

To avoid these problems there is a standard defined which ensures that all compilers which use this standard can deal with any program written to the standard. The commonly used standard is called the ANSI standard (American National Standards Institute). All the programs written in this book conform to the ANSI standard.

The ANSI standard lays out in great detail the rules governing the C language. It also defines the standard library functions which should be available to the programmer. Many compilers offer additional features and library functions which are often useful, but the use of these can mean that the program is no longer portable and will not compile successfully on other compilers.

2.12   Summary

• The hardware executes programs resident in memory which are in machine code format.

• A compiler converts high-level C program files to sections of incomplete machine code (object code) which is stored in object files.

• A linker takes all necessary object files required to produce final machine code program which is then saved in an executable file. This code can be placed in memory and executed when necessary.

• Commonly used functions are provided as precompiled code in libraries. Information required by a program to use these functions is provided in header files.

2.13   Exercises

1)   Using a suitable editor enter the "*hello world*" program discussed in section 2.8 into a file called *hello.c*. Be careful not to make any errors and type it exactly as it appears including the case of the letters. The precise indenting with spaces of some lines is not critical at this stage.

Compile the file and if there are any errors try to correct them. Once it is compiled you should be able to link and run the program. You may need to refer to the details of your compiler and linker to be able to use them.

Once the program is working, change it so that it prints the message

```
Hello Universe!
```

Note that each time you change the original source code you will need to recompile and link it before the executable file changes.

2) Here is another simple program which prints the square of a number entered by the user. Do not worry too much about all its details but enter the program carefully and compile it. The program contains four errors. Try to work out what these are from the error messages and correct them before recompiling the program.

```
/Program to print square of No. entered by user*/

#include {stdio.h}

main
{
  int n;

  printf("Enter whole number and hit return ");
  scanf("%i",&n);
  print("The value of %i squared is %i.",n,n*n);
}
```

3 Representation of Data

3.1 Introduction

In this chapter we will look at some of the most important concepts which programmers must understand if they are to be able to produce useful and reliable software. We will examine the types of data which can be stored and manipulated and how this data is represented in terms of binary digits.

We will assume that the reader has some familiarity with binary arithmetic and number bases. A complete understanding of all the details of this chapter is not essential before moving on, but a review of this chapter is recommended as the reader progresses.

3.2 Basic data types

The C language allows us to represent three basic types of data. These are integer numbers, real numbers and characters. More complex data can be represented by grouping data items of these simple types together. For example, text can be represented by strings of characters or a phone directory can be represented by a sequence of character strings and integer numbers. We will look in detail at how the basic types of data differ and how they are represented in memory in binary format. An understanding of binary representation is important, as it helps the programmer to understand the limitations of the representations and to be wary of problems which can arise.

3.3 Integer types

An integer is a whole number. For example 1, 5, 0, 123 and -56 are all integer values whereas 0.1, 2½, 123.4 and -9.9 are not. Certain types of data which are whole numbers are suitable for representation as integers in a C program. For example a person's age in years, a house number or the population of a town can all be expressed adequately as integers (e.g. 55 years, No. 12, 15230 people respectively). However, other data such as a dimension in metres, the average age of a population, or a temperature, cannot always be expressed satisfactorily as integers (e.g. 12.3 m, 34.3 years, 23.67° Celsius). It is important, when designing a program, to identify at an early stage whether an item of data is suitable for storage as an integer.

An integer is represented in most C implementations as 16 bits (2 bytes) of memory, although different implementations may use a different number of bits (check your compiler documentation). We will assume here a 16-bit representation for the sake of discussion. There are two representations available, these being signed or unsigned integers.

An unsigned integer can represent any positive whole number between the values 0 and $2^{16} - 1$ (or 65535). The representation used is that of a simple binary number. For example, for the value 12345 the bit pattern is 0000110000111001. This can be illustrated by assigning the corresponding decimal value to each bit position (i.e. ascending powers of two: 2^0, 2^1, 2^2, $2^3...2^{15}$ or 1,2,4,8...32768) as shown below:

32768	16384	8192	4096	2048	1024	512	256	128	64	32	16	8	4	2	1
0	0	1	1	0	0	0	0	0	0	1	1	1	0	0	1

Therefore, in decimal this pattern represents

$$8192 + 4096 + 32 + 16 + 8 + 1 = 12345.$$

Alternatively, a signed integer can represent positive and negative whole numbers. Using 16 bits we can represent values between $2^{15} - 1$ and -2^{15} (32767 and -32768). To represent positive numbers we use the same representation as for unsigned integers. However, since we are limiting the range to 32767 the most significant bit (i.e. left-hand bit as written) is always 0 for positive values. We could therefore use the most significant bit (MSB) to represent the sign of the number (e.g. the value 34 has the same bit pattern as -34 except that the MSB is different). This representation is called signed binary, but it presents two problems. Firstly, we have two bit patterns for zero (i.e. $+0$ and -0) which is wasteful and, secondly, numbers in this form are difficult to use in arithmetic operations such as addition. It should be appreciated that arithmetic is performed using logic gates and so we want a representation which minimises the gates required and which can be processed quickly. Therefore, a slightly different representation is used which lends itself to ease of processing; this is called two's complement.

3.4 Two's complement

In two's complement representation positive numbers are held as described for the signed binary representation where the MSB will be 0. However, to represent negative numbers we first represent the value as a positive number and then toggle all the bits (i.e. change all 1's to 0 and vice versa). Therefore, for negative numbers the MSB will always be 1. We still have a problem in that we have two bit patterns for 0 (i.e. 1111111111111111 and 0000000000000000). This is again a little wasteful and still causes problems with arithmetic involving negative values. The solution to this is to add one to a negative value after the bits are toggled (N.B. this might result in an overflow to 17 bits but this extra bit can be ignored).

To illustrate this we will consider the value −12345. We represent this initially as +12345 (0011000000111001) and then toggle all the bits to obtain 1100111111000110. Finally, one is added, using the rules of binary arithmetic to obtain 1100111111000111.

One way to view this representation is to view the MSB as representing the value −32768. Then, by summing the decimal values of each bit, we can convert the value to decimal as shown below.

− 3 2 7 6 8	1 6 3 8 4	8 1 9 2	4 0 9 6	2 0 4 8	1 0 2 4	5 1 2	2 5 6	1 2 8	6 4	3 2	1 6	8	4	2	1
1	1	0	0	1	1	1	1	1	1	0	0	0	1	1	1

−32768 + 16384 + 2048 + 1024 + 512 + 256 + 128 + 64 + 4 + 2 + 1 = −12345.

We will not concern ourselves too much with the details of binary arithmetic since it is not immediately important. However, an appreciation of how arithmetic is performed in a computer is useful knowledge and the reader may wish to follow this up by examining texts on digital logic or microprocessors (see *Microprocessor Systems*, R.J. Mitchell, Macmillan, 1995).

3.5 Self-assessment exercise − Integers

Convert the following to unsigned 16-bit binary values

a) *23456*   b) *2048*

Convert the following to 16 bit two's complement binary

c) *2048*   d) *−2048*   e) *−120*   f) *−1*   g) *−0*

Convert the following two's complement binary numbers to decimal

h) *0101010101010101*   i) *1111000011110000*

Answers:
a) 0101101110100000   b) 0000100000000000   c) 000100000000000
Positive 2's complement is same as unsigned binary   d) 1111100000000000
Toggle bits and add one. Creates 11 carries.   e) 1111111110001000
f) 1111111111111111   g) 0000000000000000 Same as +0 after conversion.
Ignore carry to bit 17.   h) 21845   i) −3856.

3.6 Short and long integers

It may be found that a 16-bit integer is not suitable for a particular application, either because we need to store values outside the range that can be represented by 16 bits, or because we are storing many small values which can be represented by fewer bits and so this would be inefficient in memory usage. In most C implementations (but not all) an integer by default is 16 bits long. In these situations we can also use short integers (which are also typically 16 bits, but may be less than standard integers in some implementations), or long integers which are typically 32 bits.

The compiler documentation will give the precise details of integer bit lengths. Some compilers may not offer long or short integers and will simply treat them as default bit length values.

Assuming that we have integer lengths of 16, 16 and 32 bits, this will give us the following ranges for unsigned and signed (i.e. two's complement) representations.

short	unsigned	0 to 65535
(16 bits)	signed	−32768 to 32767
default	unsigned	0 to 65535
(16 bits)	signed	−32768 to 32767
long	unsigned	0 to 4294967295
(32 bits)	signed	−2147483648 to 2147483647

Again, be aware that this is an illustrative example and different compilers will have different ranges. For most purposes the signed default length representation is used, as will be seen throughout this book.

3.7 Arithmetic overflow

An important issue to keep in mind when programming is the possibility of overflows. This occurs when we try to form a value which is outside the range for the particular representation used. For example, let us assume that we have two unsigned 16-bit integer values stored in memory which are 24000 and 55000. Our program then instructs the CPU to add these two numbers together and store the result back in memory as a 16-bit integer. The result will be 79000, which cannot be stored in 16 bits. This is called an overflow.

When an overflow occurs it may go undetected and the resulting value may become incorrect because bits are lost. This is obviously a serious condition and its possibility should always be kept in mind. Other programming languages often have checks built in which will detect overflows when they occur. However, C does not have this facility and this often causes problems for novice programmers.

3.8 Floating point representation

Whenever possible the use of integer representation of numbers is preferred because they can be processed quickly and they use memory space efficiently. However, in many applications we need to represent real numbers and so cannot use integer representation (e.g. the value of π cannot be represented to reasonable accuracy as a whole number). Consequently, there is another type of number representation available in C called floating point representation. Numbers in this format are stored in a fashion similar to that of the scientific notation of numbers. In scientific notation we specify a value (the mantissa) with a decimal point always after the first digit and then a power of ten (the exponent) indicating the true position of the decimal point (e.g. 2.34×10^5 or -9.45×10^{-7}).

A typical floating point value may be stored in 32 bits (4 bytes) but this again depends on the particular compiler implementation. The value may be represented as follows:

`Mantissa (24 bits)`	`Exponent (8 bits)`

where the mantissa represents a signed binary fraction (e.g. 0.11010000 represents $2^{-1} + 2^{-2} + 2^{-4} = 0.8125$) and the exponent is a signed value indicating the direction and number of digits that the binary point should be shifted to obtain the true value, just as in scientific decimal format.

A typical C implementation may use a representation with a range from around 1.2×10^{-38} to $3.4 \times 10^{+38}$ with positive or negative signs. However, an important point to remember is that the size of the mantissa is limited and so we only have at any time a precision (in this example) of 24 binary digits (equivalent to about 7 decimal places). The consequences of this can be illustrated with the following example.

Say we have a value of 2000.02 which we wish to divide by 2. When stored in memory we may find that the nearest value that can be represented is 2000.019, meaning that we have already introduced a small error into our calculation. When the CPU processes this value and produces a result which is half the original value we may find that the result requires more bits in the mantissa than are available, resulting in the least significant bits being lost or rounded up. Our final result may be something like 1000.009. Therefore, it is evident that floating point representation is not exact and rounding errors occur due to limited precision.

3.9 Double and long double representation

We saw earlier that there are different types of integer representation available which differ in the number of bits used. The same applies to floating point values where we have double and long double representations which offer greater range and precision than the default representation, but at the cost of more memory and processing time. The precise range and precision offered is again dependent on the particular compiler, but for illustration if we assume bit lengths of 24, 48 and 80 (4, 8, and 10 bytes) we may get the following (where the precision is specified in decimal digits):

float
(24 bits) $\pm1.2 \times 10^{-38}$ to $\pm3.4 \times 10^{38}$ ≈ 7 decimal digits

double
(48 bits) $\pm2.2 \times 10^{-308}$ to $\pm1.8 \times 10^{308}$ ≈ 15 decimal digits

long double
(80 bits) $\pm3.4 \times 10^{-4932}$ to $\pm1.2 \times 10^{4932}$ ≈ 19 decimal digits

The documentation for a particular compiler will give the ranges that its representations can support.

3.10 Character representation

Many computer programs are designed to process text (e.g. a word processor) and most of the programs you will write will probably at some point present messages to the user in English. Consequently, we need to be able to represent characters in binary format; this is done by assigning a binary code to each character. If we include upper and lower case letters, plus numerals, we have 58 characters which means that a single byte with 256 permutations is adequate for all these and allows for punctuation characters and some other characters called control characters.

The CPU does not 'know' about the characters themselves, all it sees are binary codes. It is the input and output hardware which is responsible for producing or interpreting the codes. For example, when the letter 'A' is struck on the keyboard the keyboard hardware sends the corresponding 8-bit binary code for 'A' to the CPU. If this letter is then to appear on the monitor then the CPU sends this code to the monitor hardware which then produces the corresponding 'A'-shaped pattern of dots on the screen.

It is obviously important that the codes used by all hardware are the same. It would be embarrassing if our computer sent out its code for the letter 'A' to a printer but the printer then interpreted this as a 'T'. Consequently, standard sets of codes are required for use by all equipment and the most commonly accepted one is called the American Standard Code for Information Interchange or ASCII. The codes defined by this standard are shown in appendix B.

The ASCII standard defines 128 characters and their codes. This could be done using seven bits, but eight are used since a byte is our basic unit of representation. In addition to the printable characters, there are a number of control characters which affect the hardware to which they are sent. An example of a control character is the carriage return character which, if sent to a printer, causes the print head to move back to the start of the line. There is also the linefeed character which advances the paper in a printer one line or moves the cursor position on the monitor down one place. There are many such control characters, but the reader will only need to be aware of a few at this stage.

3.11 Summary

- There are three basic types of binary representation of data: integer, floating point and character.

- Integers can be represented using simple binary (unsigned) for positive values or two's complement binary (signed) if negative values are required. The number of bits used can be chosen to suit the range of the values represented (short, default or long).

- Real numbers are stored using floating point representation. The number of bits used can be chosen (float, double or long double).

- Characters are represented by binary values as determined by the ASCII code. Usually one byte is required to represent a character.

- Different implementations of C may use slightly different means of representing values.

3.12   Exercises

1) Enter the following program which calculates and prints out all the powers of ten from 10^0 to 10^{12} using integer number representation. Do not worry too much about the details of this program yet. When executed, examine the results. The larger values will be incorrect or an error may be flagged. Why?

```
/* Program to print out powers of ten */
/* from 0 to 12                       */

#include <stdio.h>

main()
{
  int n,m;
  n=1;
  for (m=0;m<=12;m++)
  {
    printf("\n %i",n);
    n=n*10;
  }
}
```

2) The following program progressively multiplies a value (which is initially 1) by 10. Enter this program and run it. The resulting display is the number of iterations made followed by the new value after being multiplied by 10. What is the maximum exponent which the *float* representation can manage?

```
#include <stdio.h>

main()
{
  int m;
  float x;
  x=1;
  for (m=0;m<=12;m++)
  {
    printf("\n %i",x);
    x=x*10;
  }
}
```

Change the line *x=x*10;* to read *x=x/10;* so that now the initial value of 1 is progressively divided by ten. Re-run the program and examine the results. What is the approximate length of the mantissa in decimal digits?

4 Variables and Constants

4.1 Introduction

In the previous chapter we saw how values are represented in a computer as binary codes. In this chapter we will begin to examine how the programmer can produce programs which manipulate stored values and so perform useful functions. We will also briefly look at some input and output functions which are necessary even for the simplest of programs.

4.2 Variables

We have seen how data is represented in memory but we have not yet described how the programmer accesses and uses this data. The C language provides an easy means for the programmer to store and recall data in memory without to much concern for where it is stored or its exact representation. This is done using the concept of variables.

A variable can best be imagined as a box containing a value and which is labelled with an identifier (i.e. it is given a name). For example, we have below a variable called *number_of_apples* which contains the value 23.

```
number_of_apples
┌─────────────────────────┐
│           23            │
└─────────────────────────┘
```

There are a few points to note here. Firstly, it is useful if the identifier of the variable gives a hint as to the what the stored value represents, in this case a value representing a count of some apples. Secondly, notice that the identifier is a single word because the C language does not allow spaces in identifiers. We have used underscores for spaces instead. Thirdly, notice that this particular variable will always contain an integer value (unless we are particularly interested in fractions of apple!). Therefore, the most suitable type of data representation to use would be integer representation as described in the previous chapter. We must always indicate for each variable what type of representation it is to use (e.g. integer, floating point or character).

The advantage of a variable is that we can store and recall its value in a program just by quoting its identifier. For example, if we assume at the start of our program that there are no apples, we can indicate this with the following statement:

```
number_of_apples=0;
```

This can be read as 'set the variable called *number_of_apples* to zero'. Therefore after executing this statement our imaginary box would look like this:

```
number_of_apples
```

0

If during the course of execution of our apple counting program it is found that apples start arriving, then we need to add one each time to this variable. This can be achieved using this statement:

```
number_of_apples = number_of_apples + 1;
```

This can be read as 'the variable *number_of_apples* becomes equal to the present contents of variable *number_of_apples* plus one'. Therefore, the first time that this is executed *number_of_apples* becomes 1 (i.e. 0+1). The second time it becomes 2 (i.e. 1+1) and the third time it becomes 3 (i.e. 2+1), and so on. The contents of this 'box' can therefore be changed and updated; hence the use of the term 'variable' (i.e. it is not a fixed value).

4.3 Variable definition

When writing a program we must indicate to the compiler the names and types of any variables we intend to use. This allows the compiler and linker to reserve space in memory in which the variable will reside. This is a common convention in most languages, except BASIC, where variables are created as they are encountered in the program. To define a variable is simple. However, first we must decide on the type of the variable (i.e. is it to store integer, real or character data?) and also think up a name to use as an identifier. To define the variable from the previous example we would write:

```
int   number_of_apples;
```

This will create a 'box' (actually a space in memory) called *number_of_apples* which is large enough to contain an integer type value. We do not know the exact memory address of the variable but the compiler and linker will take care of this. All we need to do subsequently to refer to the variable is quote its identifier *number_of_apples*. If we were to require a variable which contained a real value (i.e. a floating point value) we could define it as follows:

```
float voltage;
```

This creates a space in memory large enough for a floating point type value which we can refer to by the identifier *voltage*. The general form of a simple variable definition is:

```
type identifier,identifier, ...identifier;
```

where *type* identifies the type of data representation used (integer, long integer, floating point, etc.) and the identifier is the name assigned to the variable. Notice that we can define several variables of the same type at once with a list of variable identifiers. For example:

```
int number_of_apples,number_of_figs,number_of_pears;
```

This defines three integer variables. The end of the definition is indicated by a semicolon. The type identifiers most commonly used are as follows:

`int`	signed default bit-length integer
`unsigned int`	unsigned default bit-length integer
`long int`	signed long bit-length integer
`short int`	signed short bit-length integer
`float`	default bit-length floating point
`double`	same as *float* but twice the length
`long double`	as *double* but even longer bit-length
`char`	ASCII code representation (usually 8-bits)

The position of variable definitions in programs is important. For our present purposes they must come immediately after the '*{*' symbol which follows *main ()*. We will see later that variables can be defined in other places, but for now we will stick to this rule.

4.4 Identifiers

There are certain rules governing the composition of identifiers which the programmer must keep in mind when thinking of names for variables. An identifier must be a single word and cannot contain spaces. Therefore, '*numberofapples*' is a valid identifier whereas '*number of apples*' is not. Underscore characters can be used in place of spaces to obtain names such as '*number_of_apples*'. The only characters that can be used in an identifer other than underscore are letters and digits (i.e. characters such as ?&^% cannot be used). Also, the first character of the identifier must not be a digit.

An important point concerning identifiers and all other elements of our programs is that C is case sensitive. Therefore the identifiers *Fred* and *fred* are classed as different by virtue of the differing case of the letter '*F*'. Also, identifiers must be unique and two variables cannot have the same name as each other, or be the same as any other word already used by the C language (called keywords). This is not a strictly hard and fast rule as we shall see in later chapters, but for our purposes at this stage this rule will apply.

In summary, identifiers can contain only letters, digits or underscores. The first character must not be a digit. Upper case and lower case letters are treated as being different. Identifiers cannot be keywords used by the C language. Identifiers should be unique (not a strict rule according to circumstances).

There is no limit on the length of an identifier, but some implementations may ignore everything after a certain length (often about 32 characters). This means that if two identifiers are the same for the first 32 characters but then differ, the compiler will still treat them as being the same.

4.5 A brief note on *printf* and *scanf*

So that we can illustrate the concepts of variables it will be useful to look quickly at how values can be printed on the monitor or be read from the user via the keyboard. We will examine this in greater detail in later chapters, but here is a brief introduction sufficient for present purposes.

Often our programs will produce numerical results which will reside in variables. We need to let the user know what these values are so we will need to print them on the monitor. We do this using the *printf* function. This function can be used to print messages as follows:

```
printf("Hello there!");
```

This will result in the following message appearing on the monitor:

```
Hello there!
```

Notice that the string of characters to be printed is inside brackets and quotes when written in the program but these do not appear when the message is produced. To print the value of a variable we need to indicate to *printf* what variable is to be used by quoting its identifier and also the type of the variable (e.g. *int, long int, float,* etc.). This is done using what is called a format code inside double quotes. The general format for printing the value of a variable is:

```
printf("format-code",variable-identifier);
```

For example, to print the value of an *int* variable called *apples* we would write

```
printf("%i",apples);
```

where %*i* is the format code indicating that we are printing an integer. If the variable *apples* contained the value twenty-three, then '23' would appear on the monitor when this statement was executed. To print a *float* type variable called *temperature* we would write the following:

```
printf("%f",temperature);
```

where %*f* is the format code for a *float* type variable. Notice that if we use the wrong format code for a variable (e.g. %*i* to print out *temperature*) then the results actually printed will be incorrect. Be wary of this.

We will often want to read values from the user and store them in variables for later use. To do this we use the *scanf* function which reads the keyboard and converts the keystrokes to a value which can be stored in a receiving variable. The general format is:

```
scanf("format-code",&variable identifier);
```

where again the variable identifier indicates the type of the variable to receive the value read (%*i* for *int* and %*f* for *float* variables). Notice the ampersand (&) which must precede the variable identifier. For example, we might want to read the user's age into an integer variable called *age*. To do this we might write the following:

```
printf("Please enter your age in years.");
scanf("%i",&age);
```

This prints a message prompting the user to enter their age and then the *scanf* function waits for the user to enter a number which is then stored in the variable *age* for subsequent use. If reading values into *float* type variables we must use the format code %*f*.

Notice that when using *printf* or *scanf* we must include at the top of our programs the line:

```
#include <stdio.h>
```

4.6 Case study − Resistor calculation

We require a program to read in the value of two resistances (R_1 and R_2) from the user and then to print out their combined parallel resistance (R_{para}). To do this we will need two variables to store the resistances entered by the user and another one to store the result. If we assume that we are working with resistances of whole numbers of ohms up to say 100 Ω then *int* type variables will be sufficient. To define these variables we write:

```
int r1,r2,rpara;
```

This sets up three integer 'boxes' called *r1*, *r2* and *rpara* which we can now refer to in the rest of the program. The next step is to ask the user to enter the first resistor value and then read it in. This is done as follows:

```
printf("Please enter the first resistor value.");
scanf("%i",&r1);
```

This displays an appropriate message and then reads the first value from the keyboard into variable *r1*. Next the second value is read using the following statements:

```
printf("Please enter the second resistor value.");
scanf("%i",&r2);
```

The next step is to calculate the parallel combination and store the result in the variable *rpara*. This is done with the following statement:

```
rpara=(r1*r2)/(r1+r2);
```

Note that the '*' and '/' symbols indicate multiplication and division respectively.

Finally, we must print the result in *rpara* on the monitor, along with an explanatory message using the statements:

```
printf("The combined resistance is ");
printf("%i",rpara);
```

The complete program along with a few extra embellishments is as follows:

```
/* Program to calculate resistance of two    */
/* parallel combined resistances up to 100ohms */
#include <stdio.h>

main()
{
  /* First define variables */
  int r1,r2,rpara;

  /* Prompt user for first resistance */
  printf("Please enter first resistance ");
  scanf("%i",&r1);
  /* Prompt user for second resistance */
  printf("Please enter second resistance ");
  scanf("%i",&r2);
```

```
/* Calculate result and print it */
rpara=(r1*r2)/(r1+r2);
printf("The combined resistance is ");
printf("%i",rpara);
}
```

A typical session using this program (with user responses in bold) is shown below. Notice that a 20 Ω and a 25 Ω resistor in parallel results in a resistance of 11.11 Ω. However, since we are using integer variables the fractional parts are simply lost, giving us a result of 11 Ω. (N.B. this loss of data can cause large errors; consider the result for two 1 Ω resistors.)

```
Please enter first resistance 20
Please enter second resistance 25
The combined resistance is 11
```

4.7 Numerical constants

It is very common to specify constant values (as opposed to variables) in programs. For example consider the statement

```
circumference=2.0*3.141*radius;
```

which calculates the circumference of a circle from its radius (which is stored in a variable called *radius*) by multiplying it by 2π and then storing the result in the variable called *circumference*. In this statement we have two constants, 2 and 3.141. They are constants because their values do not change each time the statement is executed, whereas the value of the variable *radius* can differ.

It is worth noting that constant values are stored using the same types of representation as variables. The type of representation used is determined by the way the value is written. For example, a constant 23 will be stored as an integer, but 34.8 will be stored as a floating point value.

For integer types we can use the suffix *U* or *u* to denote that unsigned integer representation is required and *L* or *l* to denote that a long integer is required. Also, for integer types we can use the prefix *0x* to denote that the value is written in hexadecimal or *0* to denote that it is in octal. Here are some examples of integer constants which are all of the value 234, along with the type of representation used to store them:

```
234      int or long int if value is too big for int
234U     unsigned int
234L     long int
234ul    unsigned long int
0xEA     int (234 in decimal)
```

0xEAL	*long int* (234 in decimal)
0352	*int* (234 decimal). Beware of this one!

For floating point representation the constant must contain a decimal point or must have the suffix *f*, *F*, *l* or *L*. Also, numbers with exponents are represented in floating point format. This is where numbers in scientific format are specified, such as 3.2×10^7, but in a C program this is written as *3.2e7* where the *e* or *E* replaces the '×10' part. The suffix *L* or *l* indicates that long double format is required and *F* or *f* indicates that default floating point length is required. If there is no *f*, *F*, *l* or *L* suffix then the value is represented as a *double*. Here are some examples of floating point constants:

204.3f	*float*
204.3	*double*
2.043e2	*double* (same as 2.043×10^2)
204.3L	*long double*

Much of this detail will not concern you too much at this stage. Usually, when writing a program you can simply type in the value concerned without any suffixes or prefixes and the compiler will work out what to do.

4.8 Character and string constants

To specify a single character as a constant we simply quote the character inside single quotes (e.g. *'A'* or *'?'*). Certain control characters do not have printable symbols such as carriage return and so special codes using the escape symbol '\' are used. For example the character representing newline is written as '\n'. A list of some escape sequences is shown below:

'\n'	Newline. Sends cursor to start of next line
'\a'	Alarm. Makes printer or monitor bleep
'\b'	Backspace. Moves cursor back one place
'\\'	Escape sequence for backslash character
'\''	Escape sequence for single quote character
'\ddd'	ASCII code of a character in octal (e.g. '\123' is same as 'S')
'\xhh'	ASCII code in hexadecimal (e.g. '\x08' is the same as '\b')

When strings (which can consist of any number of characters) are quoted, they must be contained within double quotes.

"Hello"

Strings may also contain escape sequences beginning with the symbol '\'.

4.9 Defining constants with *#define*

It is often the case that a constant value is used many times within a program. For example, we may have a program which uses Boltzmann's constant (k) a dozen times at different points. Rather than type in its value of 1.380662 × 10^{-23} J/K many times, which is cumbersome and error prone, we can instead associate an identifier with this value and then use this identifier rather than the actual value throughout our program. To do this we use the preprocessor directive *#define*:

```
#define   K   1.380662e-23
```

When compiled the preprocessor will first look through the program and substitute any occurrence of the identifier *k* in our program with the text '*1.30662−23*'. Note that the identifier may be longer than a single letter as used here. Therefore, if there occurs the line:

```
noise_power=4*K*273*B*R;
```

the compiled line will actually become

```
noise_power=4*1.380662e-23*273*B*R;
```

This is a useful and powerful facility, especially for constants that have values which may occasionally need to be changed (e.g. the memory address allocated to a particular peripheral device). To change the value we only need to change it in the *#define* directive and then it will automatically be changed throughout the program, thus saving time and avoiding errors.

4.10   Self-assessment test − Variables

Which of the following are valid variable identifiers:

a) `apple_pie` b) `K9`   c) `6x`   d) `Help!`   e) `apple count`

Here is a program which reads in the radius of a circle and prints its area using the formula a = πr^2. The radius and circumference may be real values. There are four errors in the program which you should be able to identify.

```
/* program to calculate area of a circle */
#include <stdio.h>
#define pi 3.14159
```

```
main()
{
  /* prompt user for radius */
  printf("Please enter radius of circle");
  scanf("%f",Radius);
  /* Calculate and print result */
  area=pi*Radius*Radius;
  printf("The area of the circle is ");
  printf("%i",area);

  /* define variables */
  float radius, area;
}
```

Answers: a) Valid. b) Valid. c) Invalid. Starts with a digit. d) Invalid. Contains '!' e) Invalid. Contains a space. Errors in program are (1) variable definitions '*float radius, area;*' in wrong place. This should come immediately after '*main() {*'. (2) Identifier '*Radius*' is used but the variable is defined as '*radius*'. Will produce undefined identifier errors. (3) The '*&*' is missing from *scanf*. Program may run but will not read values in properly. (4) "*%i*" used in *printf* to print a float value. Will not print correctly unless this is changed to "*%f*".

4.11   Summary

• Variables can be considered as 'boxes' which can hold a value.

• Each variable in a program is assigned a name (an identifier) through which it is referenced.

• Each variable in a program is assigned a type which determines the type of binary representation used to store values.

• All variables must be defined. This is where the programmer specifies the type and identifiers of variables.

• Constant values are represented according to the way they are written.

• The *#define* directive may be used to substitute an identifier with a constant value.

4.12   Exercises

1) Write a program which reads from the user three integers and prints their sum.

2) Write a program to read in two real values and print their difference.

3) Write a program to read in the values of three series capacitances and print the value of their combined capacitance. The typical range of capacitances used should be from around 1×10^{-12} F to 1 F. Hence you will need to use *float* type variables.

5 Arithmetic Operations

5.1 Introduction

Almost all programs involve some form of numerical calculations. In this chapter we will look at how to describe calculations in C programs, how they are evaluated and what can go wrong. We will begin by introducing the concept of expressions which allow us to describe arithmetic operations precisely in C.

5.2 Integer expressions

An integer expression is anything which can be evaluated to a single integer value. The following are examples of integer expressions:

```
2+2
3*(2-8)
5
8/2
```

These evaluate to 4, -18, 5 and 4 respectively (note that '*' means multiply and '/' means divide). As well as using constants in expression as above, we can also use values from variables. Suppose that in our program, we have two integer variables called *var1* and *var2* which happen to have values of 7 and 11 respectively, then we can write expressions such as:

```
2*var1
(var1+var2)/3
var2
```

These will evaluate to 14, 6 and 11. There is no limit to the complexity of expressions that we can write in C.

5.3 Floating point expressions

A floating point expression is anything which evaluates to a floating point (i.e. real) value. Some examples are:

```
3.45 + 2.3
3.0*(0.0009 + 3.4/5.0)
1.9e-4 * 6.7
```

5.4 Assignment statements

When an expression is evaluated we often want the result to be stored in a variable for future use rather than be discarded. This is done using an assignment statement such as follows:

```
answer=2+2;
```

This results in the expression being evaluated to give 4 and then this value is stored in the integer variable called *answer*. The statement can be read as 'variable *answer* becomes equal to two plus two'. The general form of an assignment statement is as follows:

```
variable_identifier = expression;
```

It is usual for the type of result from the expression (e.g. integer or floating point) to match the type of representation used by the receiving variable. However, this does not always have to be the case; we could for example assign the integer result from an integer expression to a floating point type variable. We will look at the effects of this in more detail later.

5.5 Arithmetic operators

We have available the following basic arithmetic operators

- + addition
- – subtraction
- * multiplication
- / division
- % modulo

These can be combined with constants and variables to form expressions as already shown. The first three operators shown are relatively straightforward, but the last two (division and modulo) will need some further explanation.

The effect of using division will depend on whether it operates on integer values or floating point values. Consider the following two expressions:

5/2
7.5/3.0

The first expression will be interpreted by C as division of one integer by another. When performing such a division the expression will be evaluated to yield an integer result. In this case we will get a result of 2, rather than the expected 2.5. This is because we cannot represent fractional parts using integer type representation and so anything after the decimal point is simply lost. Note that the result is not rounded to the nearest integer result, but the fractional part is simply truncated (i.e. always rounds down).

The second expression is interpreted by C as division of a floating point value by another floating point value. In this case the result produced will also be a floating point value and will be equal to 2.5. There is no rounding since floating point representation can store fractional parts. Therefore, the result of a division using integer arithmetic can be different to the result obtained using floating point arithmetic.

The modulo operator (%) can only be used with integer values. It is similar to integer division, but the value produced when it is evaluated is not the result of the division but instead the remainder from the division. For example *67%10* can be read as 'divide 67 by 10 and keep the remainder'. Therefore this evaluates to 7 and the result of the division (6) is discarded. Here are a few more examples:

```
45/10        evaluates to 4
45%10        evaluates to 5
6/10         evaluates to 0
6%10         evaluates to 6
100%10       evaluates to 0
26%4         evaluates to 2
100%40       evaluates to 20
12566%5      evaluates to 1
```

The modulo operator is useful for a number of programming 'tricks' which we will use later.

5.6 Unary + and − operators

As well as being operators for addition and subtraction the + and − symbols also represent unary operators which modify the sign of a value. As in normal everyday arithmetic the unary + operator is virtually never used. However, if a value is preceded by a − symbol its value is negated. The C compiler can distinguish between unary negation and subtraction by the position of the − symbol. Assuming that the integer variable *var1* is equal to 5 and *var2* is equal to −8 then we can write the following expressions:

```
-var1        evaluates to −5
-var2        evaluates to 8
10*-var1     evaluates to −50
var2+-var1   evaluates to −13
```

Sometimes, out of necessity or for reasons of clarity, the unary operator is included in brackets with the operand that it affects. For example:

`var2-(-var1)`   evaluates to −3

5.7 Operator precedence

It is possible to write expressions which are ambiguous in the way that they are interpreted. For example:

`4+3*2`

could be read as '4 plus 3 gives 7 times 2 gives 14' or alternatively '4 plus the product of 3 and 2 which is 6 gives 10'. To avoid such ambiguities C assigns precedence to operators. Multiply and divide have high precedence and so are always evaluated before addition and subtraction which have lower precedence. Consequently, the expression above will evaluate to 10 since the multiplication will be performed before the addition. However, we can override this by using parentheses. The evaluation of anything inside brackets takes a precedence higher than multiplication or division. Therefore, the following expression will evaluate to 14 since the contents of the brackets are evaluated first.

`(4+3)*2`

Another point worth noting here is that expressions are evaluated generally from left to right. This often causes unexpected problems which can be illustrated by the following expression:

`12/2*3`

Since multiplication and division have equal precedence the expression will be evaluated from the left. Therefore this is interpreted as '12 divided by 2 gives 6 which times 3 gives 18'. If we want to force the multiplication to be performed first then we need to use brackets as follows:

`12/(2*3)`

This now evaluates to 2. As a final note the modulo operator has equal precedence to multiplication and division.

5.8 Self-assessment test − Integer expressions

Evaluate the following integer expressions.

a) `5+24/6` b) `5*(8−2*3)` c) `5+6/2+1` d) `34/7*2` e) `1/(2*2−4)`

Evaluate the following floating point expressions to two decimal places

f) `4.5*8.7+9.7` g) `3.7*(1.9e6/(45.6+8.9)+8.5e4)`
h) `−8.7*(7.9−(−2.2))`

Below is the body of a small program. What are the values printed on the screen?

```
main()
{
  int    valueA, valueB;
  valueB=84;
  valueA=valueB%10+1;
  valueB=6+valueA/2*−4;
  printf("%i",valueA);
  printf("%i",valueB);
}
```

Answers: a) 9 b) 10 c) 9 d) 8 (34/7 evaluates to 4 with fractional part truncated) e) Will cause error and program may terminate. This evaluates to 1/0 to which there is no solution. f) 48.85 g) 443490.83 h) −87.87. In the final problem the first value printed is 5 and the second is −2.

5.9 Mathematical functions

It is a very common requirement in programming to use mathematical functions such as sine, cosine, logarithms and square roots. To perform the calculations for evaluating these functions requires a section of C program to be written. It would be very laborious for the programmer if every time he wanted to find the sine of a value he had to write a comparatively long and complex section of program to perform the calculation. Instead, prewritten sections of code to perform these functions are supplied with the compiler in a file called a library file. Each of these functions has an associated identifier (e.g. *cos* for the cosine function) which we can use as references to these functions in our program. During compilation and linking, the sections of code for the functions that we have used are copied from the library files and included where necessary in our final executable program. Using these functions consequently makes life very simple for the programmer. For example, to find the sign of an angle (in radians) we write the following expression:

```
sin(theta)
```

where *theta* is a variable representing the value of the angle. Another example may be where we wish to evaluate the sum of the natural logarithms of 2.3 and 4.5. This can be written as:

```
log(2.3)+log(4.5)
```

As we can see from the last example, references to functions can form part of larger expressions. The name of the function (e.g. *log*) is called the function identifier and the value which it is passed to work with is called an argument. There may be any number of arguments to different functions and they are contained in brackets after the function identifier. We may use variables, constants or expressions as arguments.

Most mathematical functions are written such that they return their results as double floating point type values (i.e. *double* type). They also usually require that the arguments are of *double* type. Also, note that when using the mathematical functions we must include the following line near the top of our programs:

```
#include <math.h>
```

The following functions are the ones most likely to be of immediate use are:

`sin(x)`	Sine of angle in radians
`cos(x)`	Cosine of angle in radians
`tan(x)`	Tangent of angle in radians
`asin(x)`	Arcsine in radians
`acos(x)`	Arccosine in radians
`atan(x)`	Arctangent in radians
`log(x)`	Natural logarithm
`log10(x)`	Base ten logarithm
`sqrt(x)`	Calculates the square root
`exp(x)`	Calculates exponential (i.e. e^x)
`pow(x,y)`	Calculates x to the power of y. Note this has two arguments

5.10 Case study – Complex numbers

There follows a program to read in the real and imaginary parts of a complex number (such as 2.3 + 1.7j) and print out the magnitude and argument. This requires the use of the square root function *sqrt()* and the arctangent function *atan()* to evaluate the following expressions where $\Re$ represents the real component (2.3) and $\Im$ the imaginary component (1.7).

$$magnitude = \sqrt{\Re^2 + \Im^2}$$

$$argument = atan\left[\frac{\Re}{\Im}\right]$$

Note that complex numbers rarely have integer components and also that square roots and arctangents are rarely whole numbers. Therefore we will use floating point variables throughout. Since most mathematical functions use double bit-length floating point representation (i.e. *double* type) we will actually use *double* type variables. Note that the *printf* and *scanf* format code for *double* type variables is %*lf*.

```
/* Program to read real and imaginary   */
/* parts of a complex number and print   */
/* the magnitude and argument             */

#include <stdio.h>
#include <math.h>

main()
{
    /* define variables of type 'double' */
    double real,imag,mag,arg;

    /* Read in complex number */
    printf("Please enter real component ");
    scanf("%lf",&real);
    printf("Please enter imaginary component ");
    scanf("%lf",&imag);

    /* Calculate magnitude */
    mag=sqrt(real*real+imag*imag);

    /* Calculate the argument */
    arg=atan(imag/real);

    /* Print results */
    printf("Magnitude is ");
    printf("%lf",mag);
    printf(" Argument in radians is ");
    printf("%lf",arg);
}
```

A typical session using this program would result in the following output where the user responses are shown in bold:

```
Please enter real component 3.4
Please enter imaginary component 5.6
Magnitude is 6.55133 Argument in radians is 1.02514
```

5.11 Arithmetic overflow

A common problem encountered especially when using integer arithmetic is that the final, or an intermediate result arising from a calculation is outside the range that can be stored by the particular representation used. For example, assuming that *int* type variables are sixteen bits with a range of -32768 to $+32767$ then the following section of code will cause an overflow:

```
int v1,v2,result;

v1=300;
v2=200;
result=v1*v2;
```

The value of *v1*v2* is 60000, which is too large to be stored in an *int* type variable. Unfortunately, most implementations of C do not have built in checks to detect this and the consequence is that the program will continue with some totally unexpected value assigned to the variable *result*. It is up to the programmer to anticipate such problems. One solution would be to use *unsigned int* type variables which, if implemented using sixteen bits, would have a range of 0 to 65536. However, this leaves very little safety margin if *v1* or *v2* get larger. A better solution would be to use *long int* type variables which have range of many thousand million, but at a cost of memory required and processing time.

The problem of overflow does become slightly more subtle when longer expressions are evaluated. It is often necessary to calculate intermediate results which can cause overflows even though the final result is within range. Consider this section of code which calculates the parallel combination of two integer value resistances of 300 Ω and 400 Ω using the product over sum equation.

```
int r1,r2,result;

r1=300;
r2=400;
result=(r1*r2)/(r1+r2);
```

The result that we would expect is 171 Ω, which is well within the range allowed for integer variables. However, we will obtain an unexpected result because the intermediate evaluation of the term (r1*r2) causes an overflow (120000). Again, the problem could be eased by using *long int* variables. An examination by the programmer of the likely values to be used in the calculation is always a good idea as it can highlight possible overflow problems.

Overflows are not so common when using floating point arithmetic because of their enormous ranges.

5.12　Mixed type expressions

So far, all the expressions that we have examined have consisted of a single type (e.g. values were all *int* or all *float*). When evaluating an arithmetic operation the machine can only perform the operation if the two values (operands) are of the same type. For example, the CPU can add an *int* to an *int*, multiply a *float* by a *float* or subtract a *long int* from a *long int*. However, the CPU cannot directly add a *float* to an *int* or subtract a *long int* from an *int*. It is possible to write expressions of mixed type, but this means that the CPU must first convert values from one type of representation to another in order to be able to perform the required calculations. The representation of the result will be the same as that used for the operands (e.g. an *int* plus an *int* produces an *int* result). Consider the following section of code:

```
int n,answer;
float z;

n=50;
z=1.21;
answer=n*z;
```

The expression *n*z* contains an *int* and a *float* type value which the CPU cannot immediately evaluate. The compiler has two options as to how the expression will be evaluated. The first option is to convert the value of *z* to an integer value and then use integer multiplication. However, this loses information when converting the value in *z* to an *int* type value, since this conversion involves truncating the fractional part of 1.21 to obtain 1. The final calculation would then become 50*1=50 which has a 20% error. The second option would be to convert the value of *n* to a *float* type value. This will not lose information because it will convert the value in *n* to *float* type, resulting in a temporary value of 50.0. The calculation then becomes 50.0*1.21=60.5. The second option will be the one selected by the compiler.

Notice that the value of variable *n* will not be changed in any way during the evaluation. For the purposes of the calculation a temporary copy of the value of variable *n* is converted to *float* type and is subsequently discarded.

The calculation above which involves multiplying a *float* by a *float* type value will produce a *float* type result. This result which is stored temporarily must then be assigned to variable *answer*, but this is an *int* type variable. The CPU is then forced to convert the result of 60.5 to *int* type representation which involves truncation of fractional parts. This is perfectly legitimate but the programmer should be aware that information is being lost and consider the consequences. The final result placed into variable *answer* will therefore be 60.

As a rule, whenever an operation requires conversion of a value from one type to another the compiler always chooses the option which will not lose information. Therefore, integer representations will be converted to floating point representation. Also, if we had a case where we added an *int* and a *long int* then conversion of the *long int* value to *int* type might lose information. Therefore, the compiler will instead choose to convert the *int* to *long int*, which cannot cause information loss.

5.13   Type casting

Type casting allows us to override the choice that the compiler makes about the type conversions made when evaluating mixed expressions. A type cast has the following format:

```
(type) operand
```

where *type* is a type identifier (e.g. *int, double, char*) and the operand is the value which we want to have converted to this type. Consider the following example:

```
int a,result;
double x;

a=10;
x=23456;
result=a*log10(x);
```

In this example the function *log(x)* is called which returns a double floating point value of 4.3703. The next stage of evaluation involves multiplying the intermediate *double* type value by an *int* type value. The compiler will therefore choose to convert the *int* to a *double* and then perform the multiplication, giving a result of 10.0*4.3703=43.703. This is then assigned to the integer variable *result* which means that the final value is truncated to 43.

We can cause the expression to be performed differently if it as written as:

```
result=a*(int)log10(x);
```

In this case the *log* function is called and returns a *double* value of 4.3703 as before. However, we have preceded this with an *int* type cast and so this intermediate result is then converted (with loss of information) to the *int* type value of 4 via truncation. The next step involves the multiplication of two *int* type values giving in an *int* type result of 10*4=40. This can then be assigned to the *int* variable *result* without any conversion. We therefore get a totally different result simply by changing the way the expression is evaluated.

It is unlikely that novice programmers will need to use type casting often, but it illustrates that care must be taken when writing expressions, as all may not be as it first seems.

5.14   Self-assessment test − Mixed expressions

Evaluate the resulting values of the variables a, b, c, d, e and w, x, y, z in the following section of program:

```
int    a,b,c,d,e,I1,I2;
long int L1;
double w,x,y,z,D1;

I1=5;
I2=22;
L1=1000000;
D1=2.3456;

a=D1*I1;
b=D1*(I2/I1);
c=(9.8+I1)*I2;
d=L1*I1/I2;
e=I2*sqrt(D1*I1);

w=D1+I2/I1;
x=D1+I2/(float)I1;
y=(int)D1+I1;
z=(int)(20*cos(D1));
```

Answers:
a) *I1* converted to *double* to obtain 11.728. Assigned to *int* variable so result is 11.   b) *I2/I1* evaluated as *int* to obtain *int* value of 4. This is then converted to *double* and multiplied by *D1* to obtain 9.3824. This is then assigned to an *int* variable to obtain 9.   c) The constant 9.8 is held in *double* format, therefore *I1* is converted to *double* to obtain 14.8. *I2* must also then be converted to *double* and we obtain 325.6. Final result in *int* variable *c* is therefore 325.   d) *L1*I1* is evaluated first, so *I1* is converted to *long int*. This gives a *long int* value of 5000000. *I2* must then also be converted to *long int* and we obtain a result of 227272. However, when this is assigned to the *int* variable *d* it is too large (assuming an *int* is 16 bits) and we will cause an overflow, meaning that the

value of *d* is unpredictable.   e) First evaluated is *D1*I1* which results in the *double* value 11.728. The square root function then returns the *double* value 3.4246. *I2* is then converted to a *double* and we obtain 75.342. Therefore variable *e* becomes 75.   w) *I2/I1* is evaluated as integers to obtain 4. This is then converted to *double* and the final *double* value assigned to *w* is 6.3456. x) *I1* is first converted to a *float* value. The division therefore also requires *I2* to be converted to a *float*, resulting in a *float* value of 4.4. Next this *float* value is converted to a *double* (therefore remains 4.4) and added to *D1*. Variable *x* therefore becomes 6.7456.   y) *D1* is converted to the *int* value 2 and added to *I1* to obtain the *int* value 7. This must then be converted to *double* when assigned to variable *y* which becomes 7.0000.   z) *cos(D1)* returns a *double* value of -0.6996. The integer constant 20 is then converted to *double* and we obtain -13.9915. The *int* type cast then converts this to the *int* value of 13. On assignment to the *double* variable *z* it is converted to the *double* value 13.0000.

5.15   Increment and decrement operators

It is a very common in programming to need to increment a variable (i.e. add one). For example, to add one to the *int* variable *n* we could write:

```
n=n+1;
```

which is interpreted as '*n* becomes equal to the present value of *n* plus one'. We can use a shorthand notation in C which can be used to replace the statement above with:

```
n++;
```

When executed this will cause the value of *n* to be incremented by one. Similarly, to decrement a variable (i.e. subtract one) we can write:

```
n--;
```

Note that the increment and decrement operators can only be used with integer or character type variables. When used on *char* type variables the value of the variable is shifted one position through the ASCII code sequence.

5.16   Summary

- An arithmetic expression is any combination of variables, constants, function references and mathematical operators which can be evaluated to a single value.

- An assignment is a statement in which a value of an expression is placed in an identified variable.

- All operators are assigned precedence which determines the order in which expressions are evaluated. Expressions are evaluated from left to right unless operator precedence dictates otherwise.

- Common mathematical functions are made available through the use of libraries.

- Arithmetic overflows can occur without detection in C programs. Therefore, the programmer should consider if circumstances might arise which can cause overflows.

- In mixed type expressions the compiler will select conversions which will not cause loss of data. This generally means converting to a representation with a larger bit length and converting integer types to floating point types. Programmers should consider the consequences of this.

- Type casting can be used to cause type conversions other than those automatically selected by the compiler.

5.17   Exercises

1)   The roots of a quadratic equation of the form $ax^2 + bx + c = 0$ can be found using the well known equation

$$x = \frac{-b \pm \sqrt{b^2 - 4ac}}{2a}$$

Write a program which reads in three real values representing a, b and c and then prints the two values of x which are the roots. Notice that the equation above is actually two separate equations each of which will need to be evaluated separately. As an example the value of $1, -1$ and -6 for a, b and c respectively should yield the results -2 and 3. What happens if the values of 2, -1 and 4 are used?

2)   The frequency response of a simple RC low-pass filter is given by the expression:

$$T(jw) = \frac{1}{1 + j\dfrac{f}{f_o}}$$

The voltage gain and phase responses can be derived from this and are found to be:

$$|T(jw)| = \frac{1}{\sqrt{1 + \left[\dfrac{f}{f_o}\right]}}$$

$$\phi(w) = -\arctan\left[\frac{f}{f_o}\right]$$

Write a program which reads a value of frequency from the user and then prints the gain and phase shift of a filter with a cutoff frequency (f_o) of 1 kHz. Two values for the gain should be printed, one being the result of the equation above and the second being the same value expressed in dB.

6 Control of Program Flow

6.1 Introduction

All of the programs that we have examined so far have been very simple in that they have executed statements from beginning to end one after the other in a linear manner. If it was only possible to write this type of program then it would barely be worth the effort, because the power of a computer lies in its ability to perform repetitive tasks quickly. A good programming language must reflect this fact. Also, none of our programs has required the computer to make any decisions. This is another important feature which allows our programs to act according to circumstances. All programming languages have facilities for decision making and repetitive processing through the provision of program flow control, which is the subject of this chapter.

6.2 The *if* statement

The *if* statement allows the CPU to make a decision and then, according to the result, it can take one of two routes through the subsequent program. The general form of a simple *if* statement is

```
   if (condition) single-statement;
or
   if (condition)
   {
     statement;
     statement;
        .
        .
        .
   }
```

Notice that there are two forms; the first allows us to control whether or not a single statement is executed and the second allows us to control whether a whole sequence of statements between brackets is executed. An example of the use of an *if* statement may be to check that a value provided by a user is valid. For example, let us assume that we require the user to enter an positive integer value. If a negative value is entered we need to print a message telling the user that they are in error. This section of program might appear as follows:

```
   int n;

   printf("Please enter a positive whole number. ");
   scanf("%i",&n);
   if (n<0) printf("Error. Value was negative");
```

In this program the value of variable *n* is read from the keyboard. The *if* statement then performs a test to determine if *n* is less than zero (i.e. negative). If this is true then the *printf* statement that follows is performed. If the test result is false then the *printf* statement is skipped. In either case the program then continues with whatever program statement follows after the entire *if* statement. Therefore, if the user enters '3' then no message is printed, but if they enter '−9' then the message *'Error, Value was negative'* will appear.

6.3 Boolean expressions

Before we continue looking at program control statements we need to look a little harder at how we can program the machine to make decisions. Such decisions are based usually on the values of variables (e.g. is variable *x* greater than 10? or is variable *y* equal to 5?). We write such expressions in the form of a boolean expression, which is any expression that can be evaluated to a true or false value. The result of this evaluation can then be used to determine which route to take through the program as we have seen with the *if* statement. Here are some examples of simple boolean expressions:

`x>3`	is variable *x* greater than 3?
`y==4`	is variable *y* equal to 4?
`y<=x`	is variable *y* less than or equal to variable *x*?
`x!=7`	is variable *x* not equal to 7?

Assuming that we know the values in variables *x* and *y* then these can be evaluated to true or false. We can make up more complex expressions using the logical AND operator (*&&*) and the logical OR operator (*||*). For example:

`x<7 && y==9`	*x* less than 7 AND *y* equal to 9
`x==6 || x==9`	*x* equal to 6 OR *x* equal to 9
`!(x==6 || x==9)`	*x* not equal to 6 or 9
`y>=1 && y<=100`	*y* between 1 and 100

The following operators are available in boolean expressions:

`==`	Equality. Do not use a single equals sign (i.e. '=').
`!=`	Not equal.
`>`	Greater than.
`<`	Less than.
`>=`	Greater or equal.
`<=`	Less than or equal.
`!`	Not (i.e. inverts result). A unary operator.

&&   Logical AND
| | Logical OR

There is an order of evaluation of boolean expressions similar to that used in arithmetic expressions. The NOT operator (*!*) is always evaluated first, followed by the relational operators (==, <=, >= etc.), followed by AND (&&) and then OR (| |). However, we can use parentheses to alter the order of evaluation in the same manner as we can in arithmetic expressions. For example:

```
x>=1 || x<=100 && y==10
```

at first appearance suggests that this expression is true if *x* is between 1 and 100 AND *y* equals 10. However, since the && operator has a higher precedence than | | then this is interpreted as '*x* less than 10 AND *y* equal to 100, OR *x* greater or equal to 1'. If *y* was not 10 this would still evaluate to true for any value of *x* greater or equal to 1. We can force the OR to be evaluated first using brackets as follows:

```
(x>=1 || x<=100) && y==10
```

The order of precedence of operators is shown below. Those with highest precedence are shown first and any of equal precedence are on the same line.

```
!
&&
||
==, !=, <, >, <=, >=
```

Always beware of using a single equals sign when testing for equality. Consider the example:

```
n=2+3;
if (n=4) printf ("The answer is 4);
```

In this section of code the first statement will clearly assign the value 5 to variable *n*. The subsequent *if* statement would appear to read 'if the variable *n* is equal to 4 then execute the following *printf* statement'. However, a single equals is always interpreted as an assignment and so the section '*n=4*' is actually read as 'set variable *n* to 4' even though it forms part of an *if* statement. Therefore, the value of *n* is changed by the *if* statement and the decision over the flow of control is not immediately predictable. Therefore, the message may be printed even though *n* was originally 5. This is a very common programming error which is easily made. The *if* statement should actually be:

```
if (n==4) printf ("The answer is 4");
```

It is worth noting that the result of a boolean expression is stored using integer type representation. A value of zero represents false and any other value represents true. It is possible to assign the result of a boolean expression to an integer variable and use the value in subsequent expressions.

6.4 *if-else* statement

An extension to the *if* statement allows a selection of which of two sections of code is executed. The general form of such a statement is

```
if (condition) statement;
else statement;
```

or

```
if (condition)
{
  statement;
  statement;
     .
     .
     .
}
else
{
  statement;
  statement;
     .
     .
     .
}
```

If the condition is evaluated as true then the statement or statement sequence which immediately follows the condition is executed. However, if the evaluation result is false then the statement or statement sequence after the word *else* is executed instead. Therefore, we can select between two sections of code. In either circumstance the flow of control will then continue after the end of the entire *if-else* statement.

An example of the use of an *if-else* statement is shown below. This is a section of a program which reads a value and prints its square root using the *sqrt* function. There is nothing to prevent the user entering a negative value for which there is no square root. Therefore, if the value is negative we do not want to call the square root function (which could behave unpredictably) but rather print an explanatory message.

```
/* Define double type variables */
double x, result;

/* Prompt user for value and read it */
printf("Please enter a value.");
scanf("%lf",&x);

/* Value read into x. Now test its sign */
if (x<0)
{
  /* value is negative so print message */
  printf("Negative values have no square root.");
}
else
{
  /*Value is positive so calculate and print root */
  result=sqrt(x);
  printf("Square root is");
  printf("%lf",result);
}
```

In this example, whole blocks of statements between *{}* symbols are used to indicate the two sections of code which are under the control of the *if-else* statement. Also, notice the indenting used to make the beginning and ends of the two blocks of statements more obvious. This is not required by the compiler but makes the program easier for the programmer to follow. We will say more about indenting later.

6.5 Self-assessment test — Boolean expressions

Assuming that the values of the variables a and b are 5 and 10 respectively, then evaluate the following expressions to true or false:

a) a==5   b) a<100   c) !(b>=15)   d) b=4   e) a>=b
f) a!=b   g) (a>10)||(b==10)   h) (a<10)&&(b<5)
i) (a==5)&&(b==10)   j) !((a!=5)||(b!=10))
k) ((a==5)||(a==b))&&(b<100)

What will be the resulting value displayed on the screen by the following code if the user enters a value of 25 and then −25?

```
double x,y;
scanf("%lf",&x);
if (x>=0.0)
{
  y=sqrt(x);
}
```

```
else
{
  x=-x;
  y=sqrt(x);
}
printf("%lf",y);
```

Answers: a) True. b) True. c) True. NOT operator inverts result. d) Invalid. Should be 'b==4' which is false. e) False. f) True. g) True due to second term. h) False due to second term. i) True. j) True. This expression is exactly equivalent to the previous problem. It illustrates De Morgan's theorem, often used in digital electronic design. k) True. Result of OR is true which is then 'ANDed' with another true term.

For the value 25 the square root is calculated and printed. For −25 the value is first made positive (+25) and again the square root is calculated and printed. We therefore get '5.000' printed in either case.

6.6 *for* loop

We will now look at how we can write programs to perform repetitive tasks using loops. There are three types of loop available in C which we will discuss in turn. We will begin with the *for* loop which has the general form:

```
for(initial value,continuation expression,increment)
{
  statement;
  statement;
      .
      .
      .
}
```

Note that if the loop only contains a single statement we can omit the *{}* symbols. The action of this loop is best illustrated using an example. Suppose that we want to print all the values from 1 to 10. We could use ten *printf* statements but this would be laborious. Instead, by using the *for* loop below we can use the same *printf* statement ten times.

```
int n;

for (n=1;n<=10;n++)
{
  printf("%i ",n);
}
printf("Done");
```

The *for* loop can be interpreted as 'initialise *n* to 1 and then while *n* is less than or equal to 10 execute the statements in the following brackets while adding one to *n* each time'. Therefore, when the loop is first executed the variable *n* which acts as a counter is set to one. Then the continuation expression is evaluated (i.e. it tests if *n* is less than 10). If the result is true then the code between the *{}* symbols is executed and so '1' will be printed by *printf*. When the *}* symbol is reached, one is added to the variable *n* (note that we have used the increment operator *n++*) and then flow returns to the start of the loop where the conditional expression is re-evaluated. This time *n* has the value 2, meaning that the conditional expression is still true, and so we again execute the statements between the *{}* symbols resulting in '2' being printed. The variable *n* is then incremented again and the process repeats. After the tenth pass through the loop, *n* will be equal to 11, and so on return to the start of the loop the conditional expression will become false. In this case the loop terminates and the program flow continues after the end of the whole *for* statement (i.e. after the *}* symbol). The printed result is:

```
1 2 3 4 5 6 7 8 9 10 Done
```

Another example might be to add all the odd numbers between 1 and 20. In this case the program might appear as follows:

```
int m,total;

total=0;
for (m=1;m<20;m=m+2)
{
    total=total+m;
}
printf("%i",total);
```

In this case the control part of the loop is interpreted as 'set *m* to 1 and then while *m* is less than 20 execute the loop while adding 2 to *m* each time'. Note that the increment this time is an assignment of the form '*m* becomes equal to *m* plus 2'. Each time around the loop we add the value of *m* (1, 3, 5, 7, etc.) to the running total in variable *total*. The final value printed will be 100 (i.e. $1+3+7+...+19$).

Notice an important side issue here. We have included the statement *total=0;* to ensure that the value in variable *total* is zero before we start adding to it the values of variable *m*. Up to this point we do not know what value is in the variable *total*, since C does not guarantee to initialise variables to any particular value and so we must ensure that it is zero initially. We do not need to do this for variable *m* since it is set to 1 at the start of the *for* loop.

It is possible to have loops within loops (i.e. nested). Suppose we want a program to print the sum all the numbers from 1 to all the numbers from 1 to

10 (i.e. we want to print the values of 1, 1+2, 1+2+3, 1+2+3+4, 1+2+3+4+5 up to 1+2+3+...+10). This needs two *for* loops. The first (outer) loop sets the upper limit of the sum (i.e. loops from 1 to 10), while each time the inner loop calculates the sum from 1 to the current upper limit. The program will appear as follows:

```
int sum,limit,n;

for (limit=1;limit<=10;limit++)
{
  sum=0;
  for (n=1;n<=limit;n++)
  {
    sum=sum+n;
  }
  printf("%i ",sum);
}
printf("Done");
```

The inner loop of this example is similar to the previous example. However, the value which determined how many times this loop iterates is contained in the variable *limit*, which assumes the value from 1 to 10 under the control of the outer loop. The results printed are:

```
1 3 6 10 15 21 28 36 45 55 Done
```

Readers are recommended to work through this example carefully on paper until they understand what is happening.

Notice that generally we control *for* loops by counting the number of iterations. Therefore, the controlling variable should be of an integer type. Also, beware of a common error as illustrated below:

```
for (n=1;n<=10;n++);
{
  printf("%i ",n);
}
```

It would be expected that this loop would print all the values from 1 to 10. Instead it simply prints the single value of 11. This is because of the extra semicolon at the end of the first line. This indicates that this is the end of the *for* loop. Consequently, we execute an empty loop 10 times and then the following code in brackets is only executed once, as it is not considered to be in the loop. We therefore only get printed the value of *n* after the loop has completed. Removal of the extra semicolon will rectify the problem.

6.7 *do-while* loop

The *for* loop is useful when we know how many times we need to iterate around the loop. However, there are cases when we will need a loop, but we do not know initially how many times the loop needs to run. In this case we can use a *do-while* loop which has the following general form:

```
do
{
  statement;
  statement;
     .
     .
}
while (condition);
```

The word *do* is used to indicate that we are beginning a loop, followed by the body of the loop within *{}* symbols (note that we can dispense with the *{}* symbols if the loop contains only one statement). The end of the loop is marked by the word *while* and a conditional expression which, if evaluated as true, sends the program flow back around the loop. If the condition is false, then the program flow continues after the end of the entire *do-while* statement. A example may be where we need the user to enter an odd integer value. If they enter an even value the program must try reading another value. The section of code to do this is as follows:

```
int oddval;
do
{
  printf("Please enter an odd value");
  scanf("%i",&oddval);
}
while (oddval%2==0);
```

In this section of program we enter the loop and read a value into the variable *oddval*. At the end of the loop we test to see if the number is even or odd. We use the modulo operator (%) here which returns the remainder of the division of *oddval* by two. If the remainder is 0 then the value is even and we loop back to read another value into *oddval*. If the remainder is not 0 then the only other possibility is that it was 1, indicating that the value was odd. The program will therefore continue after the end of the loop.

Another example, which is often a useful feature of programs, is to loop around the entire program to give the user the option of re-running or terminating the program. This could be done as follows:

```
main()
{
  char keypressed;
  do
  {
    (main body of program)
      .
      .
    printf("Do you wish to re-run program?");
    printf("Hit 'y' to re-run, other key to quit");
    scanf("%c",&keypressed);
  }
  while (keypressed=='y' || keypressed=='Y');
  printf("Program terminating");
}
```

This example uses a character variable (*char* type) called *keypressed* to store a response from the user. When the program runs it enters the *do-while* loop and runs the main body of the program which performs some task. Once this is completed it prompts the user to indicate whether they would like to finish or re-run the whole program. It then reads a character from the keyboard using *scanf* with the format code *'%c'*, indicating that it is reading in a character. At the end of the loop it then tests if the contents of the variable *keypressed* is an upper or lower case 'y'. If this is true then the program flow will loop back to the start of the loop and consequently the main body of the program is re-run. If the result is false, it does not loop back and prints a final message before the program ends.

6.8 *while* loop

A *while* loop is vary similar to a *do-while* loop, except that the test which determines if the body of the loop is executed is performed at the start of the loop rather than at the end. The general format is as follows:

```
while (condition)
{
  statement;
  statement;
    .
    .
}
```

Note that if the loop contains only one statement the *{}* symbols can be omitted.

An example is shown below in which the user is required to enter a value between 1 and 10 (inclusive), which is then used further on in the program. This section reads the value and checks that it is in the correct range. If not, then an error message is printed and the value is re-read.

```
int n;
n=0;
while (n<1 || n>10)
{
  printf("Enter a value between 1 and 10");
  scanf("%i",&n);
  if (n<1 || n>10)
  {
    printf("Not in correct range. Try again");
  }
}
```

In this example *n*, which is to hold the value entered by the user, is set to zero initially and then a test is performed in the *while* statement to see if *n* is less than one or greater than ten. Since this is initially true the body of the loop executes. It then prompts the user to enter a value which is then read into variable *n*. An *if* statement then tests if the new value of *n* is between 1 and 10 and, if not, prints an error message. The program then reaches the end of the loop and returns to the start where again *n* is tested to see if it is between 1 and 10. If it is not, then the entire loop will re-run, causing a new value to be read. If the value of *n* is in the desired range the body of the loop is skipped and the program flow continues to whatever follows.

Note that this section of code could be written slightly more efficiently using a *do-while* loop and the reader may find it a useful exercise to do this.

6.9 Choice of loop type

Each of the three types of loop has its own particular characteristics, making each suited to particular circumstances. Therefore, when writing a program we want to select the most appropriate type. There now follows some guidelines to help make this decision.

In circumstances where at the start of the loop it is known how many times the loop will execute, we use a *for* loop. This type of loop is controlled by a variable which can be used to count the number of iterations of the loop. We may not know how many times the loop needs to execute when writing the program, but this might only become apparent as the program runs (e.g. as a result of user input). Therefore, if the number of iterations will be known at the time that the loop will execute, then a *for* loop should be used.

In circumstances where it is not necessarily known how many times the loop will run, we use a *do-while* or a *while* loop. Such circumstances may arise when waiting for an external event to occur. A *do-while* loop makes its decision as to whether to continue looping at the end of the loop and therefore the loop is guaranteed to run at least once. A *while* loop makes its decision at the start of the loop and may not execute the body of the loop at all if the test fails the first time around. In general, the *do-while* loop is the most useful and only a few situations lend themselves better to the *while* loop.

6.10   Indentation

It is worth returning at this point to the idea of indentation. The reader will have noted that all the program examples containing *if* and loop statements include sections of code which are indented a few spaces. This is not a requirement of the C compiler, but is a convention adopted to make it easier for the programmer to follow the structure of the program. The indentation is to help identify the start and end of a section of code which is under the control of an *if* statement or which is the body of a loop. In large programs, a section of code many be yards long when printed which makes indentation vital to be able to locate the start and end.

A section of code to be indented will begin with a { symbol and end with a } symbol. The usual convention is that, following a { symbol, all statements are indented (usually by four or eight spaces) until the corresponding } symbol is reached, whereupon the indentation finishes. Since we can have loops within loops, then we may have nested levels of indentation.

There are plenty of examples throughout this book which demonstrate indentation. The novice programmer is strongly advised to indent all programs, since it is not only good practice, but it can also help to highlight errors due to mismatching { and } symbols.

6.11   Case study − Guessing game

The program which follows is a simple game in which the computer 'thinks' of a number between 1 and 10 and then the user must guess this value. The game continues until the user gets the answer right and then his number of attempts is printed. Finally, the user can opt to play another game or quit the program.

The first problem is to make the machine 'think' of a number between 1 and 10 seemingly at random. An easy way to do this is to use a function called *time* which returns the number of seconds which have elapsed since 1 January 1970. This will be a large integer number and so the value returned is of *long int* type. This value will clearly be different each time the program is run but it is not in the range 1 to 10. To extract a value in the correct range we can write

```
answer=time(NULL)%10;
```

Do not worry to much about the *NULL* argument for the *time* function, but it is required for it to work correctly. The *time* function might return a value such as 473048753 which we then divide by ten and keep the remainder by use of the modulo operator (%). The result would then be 3 which is in the range we require. In fact, whatever value the time function returns we will always get a value assigned to the variable *answer* between 0 and 9. To obtain a range from 1 to 10 we can then simply add one.

We will want to check that values entered by the user are valid and so when reading user responses we might include a loop as follows:

```
do
{
  printf("Enter your guess between 1 and 10");
  scanf("%i",guess);
  if (guess<1 || guess>10)    printf("Invalid!");
}
while (guess<1 || guess>10)
```

This will re-read the user's response and print an error message if the value is not between 1 and 10 inclusive. The whole program is as follows:

```
/*Simple guessing game where machine thinks of a    */
/*number from 1 and 10 which the user must guess     */

#include <stdio.h> /* Needed for printf and scanf */
#include <time.h>  /* Needed for time function */

main()
{
  int answer, guess, attempts;
  char keypressed;

  /* Start of loop around whole program */
  do
  {
    /* Machine thinks of a number   */
    answer=time(NULL)%10+1;
    printf("I have thought of a number.");
    printf("\nCan you guess what it is?");

    /* Play the game.Loop until guess is correct */
    attempts=0;
    do
    {
      attempts++;   /*Increment count of attempts*/

      /* Read user response */
      do
      {
        printf("\nEnter guess between 1 and 10");
```

```
        scanf("%i",&guess);
        if (guess<1 || guess>10)
          printf("Invalid!");
    }
    while (guess<1 || guess>10);

    /* User value now read. Print message and */
    /* loop back if incorrect                 */
    if(guess!=answer)
       printf("Incorrect. Try again");
    }
    while (guess!=answer);

    /*User guessed correctly. Print message and */
    /*re-run if user wishes                      */
    printf("Correct!! Number of attempts was ");
    printf("%i",attempts);
    printf("\nHit R to re-run, other key to quit");
    fflush(stdin);
    scanf("%c",&keypressed);
  }
  while (keypressed=='r' || keypressed=='R');
}
```

Notice two small things used here which have not so far been covered. The use of \n inside *printf* messages causes the cursor position to move to the start of the next line; this tidies up the output. Also, a function called *fflush* has been called before the final *scanf*. When reading characters with *scanf*, problems can occur because of the buffer often associated with the keyboard. This issue is covered later but the inclusion of the *fflush* before the *scanf* statement should eradicate any problems. A typical game may result in the following dialogue:

```
I have thought of a number.
Can you guess what it is?
Enter guess between 1 and 10. 3
Incorrect. Try again
Enter guess between 1 and 10. 11
Invalid!
Enter guess between 1 and 10. 6
Incorrect. Try again
Enter guess between 1 and 10. 2
Correct!! Number of attempts was 3
Press R to re-run, other key to quit X
```

6.12 Summary

- Program flow is controlled by decisions based on boolean expressions.

- *if* statements allows optional execution of a section of code.

- *if-else* statements allow one of two sections of code to be selected for execution. These statements are not commonly required and simple *if* statements are usually sufficient.

- *for* loops allow a section of code to be executed repeatedly for a known number of iterations.

- *do-while* and *while* loops allow a section of code to be repeated until some event or circumstance arises. *do-while* loops are more suitable than *while* loops for the majority of tasks that usually arise.

- Indentation should be used so that sections of code under the control of loops or *if* statements can be easily identified.

Note that there are other program flow statements such as *switch, goto, ?* and *break* which the interested reader may wish to research. However, for our present purposes those covered in this chapter are sufficient.

6.13 Exercises

1) Write a program to print all the values from 1 to 100 using a *for* loop.

2) Repeat exercise 1, but instead of using a *for* loop use a *do-while* and then a *while* loop. You will need to use a variable to count the iterations.

3) Write a program to add all the even numbers from 1 to 1000. It is actually possible to do this in your head in just a few seconds using a short cut trick, but write a loop to do it the long way.

4) The factorial of a number (!) is defined as follows for positive integers:

```
1!   1
2!   1*2=2
3!   1*2*3=6
4!   1*2*3*4=24
5!   1*2*3*4*5=120
etc.
```

The program below reads in an integer and calculates the factorial. Entering a value of 6 should give a result of 720, but this is not the case since there is one small error in the program. Enter this program and then study it so that you can make the one very small change to rectify the error.

```
#include <stdio.h>
  main()
  {
    int n,loop,fact;

    scanf("%i",&n);
    fact=0;
    for (loop=1;loop<=n;loop++)
    {
      fact=fact*loop;
    }
  printf("%i",fact);
  }
```

5) Write a guessing game program in which the machine thinks of a number between 1 and 100 and then accepts guesses from the user until they make a correct guess. If the guess is incorrect, the machine should respond by telling the user if their guess was too low or too high. When the program is working in a simple form, extend it such that user input is checked for validity, a count of the attempts made is printed, and the option to play another game is available without quitting the program.

6) Write a program to play the game described in section 6.11 but where the roles are reversed. That is, the user thinks of a number and the machine makes guesses. The user will respond by pressing 'H' if the guess is too high, 'L' if too low or 'C' if correct. This means using *scanf* with a *"%c"* format code to read a character from the keyboard. The machine should act intelligently in making guesses and use the most efficient means of finding the answer.

7) As an addition to the program in sectiont 6.11 make the program detect if the user has cheated by changing the number he has thought of during the game.

7 Input and Output

7.1 Introduction

We will examine in this chapter how our programs can interact with a user by displaying results and messages on the monitor and by reading information from the keyboard. There are many ways that a computer can interact with the real world when controlling equipment or reading the output of various sensors directly, but here we will only concern ourselves with interaction with a user of a program via the keyboard and monitor. The principal means of input and output (I/O) are the *printf* and *scanf* functions. These are complex and very powerful functions and there is much that can go wrong when using them. Consequently, we will not look exhaustively at these functions, but concentrate on using them in a simple manner which is sufficient for our needs and which will hopefully keep our programs error free. We will also look at a few other I/O functions, in addition to *scanf* and *printf*.

7.2 Data types

One of the most common problems encountered by novices with I/O functions a to failure to understand and appreciate that all our variables are of particular types and the type determines how its value is represented in memory. Remember that we have the following commonly used basic data types with the typical bit lengths shown:

`int`	16-bit two's complement integer
`long int`	32-bit two's complement integer
`unsigned int`	16-bit simple binary integer
`char`	8-bit ASCII character code
`float`	32-bit floating point format
`double`	64-bit floating point format

This means that if we store the value '2' in an integer variable and '2.0' in a floating point variable the resulting pattern of bits is entirely different in each (and also of different lengths!). This is an important principle to keep in mind.

7.3 Output using *printf*

The *printf* function is our principal means of displaying a message or a value on the screen (or on a printer if required). A simple case of its use is to print a string:

```
printf ("Hello");
```

which results in the following appearing on the screen:

```
Hello
```

This is a useful mode in which to use *printf*, but we would not get very far if this was all that it was capable of performing. We will often be required to print the values contained in variables, which means that we must instruct *printf* to look at the value of a variable, convert the value from its bit pattern representation to a string of numerals that the user can understand, and then send the result to the monitor hardware. Consider the following program:

```
#include <stdio.h>
main ()
{
    int a,b,result;

    a=2;
    b=3;
    result=a+b;
    printf ("2 plus 3 is %i",result);
}
```

Notice the inclusion of header file *stdio.h* which should be included whenever using *printf* or *scanf*.

In this program we define two integer variables and set them to 2 and 3. We then calculate the sum of these two values and store the answer in the integer variable called *result*. We then want to print an appropriate string to display the result of the calculation. This string starts off as "*2 plus 3 is ...*". However, at this point we do not know what comes next when we are writing our program (assuming our arithmetic is very poor!) so we must instruct *printf* to insert into the string the value stored in the variable *result*. To do this we place in the string (which is referred to as the format string) the code %*i*. The % symbol is treated by *printf* as a special symbol indicating that a value is to be substituted into the string as it is printed. In this case we have %*i*, which tells *printf* that the value to be placed in the string is an integer. We then close the format string with quotes. However, we must then tell *printf* where to find the value that it is to substitute in the place of the %*i* code. This is done after the end of the format string, where we give the name of the variable *result* which contains the value to be printed. The resulting message displayed is:

```
2 plus 3 is 5
```

This is all well and good until we change the line *a=2* to *a=4*. Our sophisticated and expensive computer will then display the message:

```
2 plus 3 is 7
```

Obviously this is not satisfactory. What we need to do here is also print the contents of the variables *a* and *b*, rather than 'hard-write' these values into the *printf* format string. We can modify our printf statement to become:

```
printf("%i plus %i is %i",a,b,result);
```

This prints the message with three integer values substituted. The substitutions occur in the order in which the variables are specified after the format string. With *a=4* and *b=3* we get the more reassuring message:

```
4 plus 3 is 7
```

7.4 *printf* format codes

In the above example we used the format code *%i*, which tells *printf* to take the specified value that is stored in memory as a series of 16 bits representing the value in binary two's complement (i.e. an *int* type) and convert it to a string of numerals on the screen representing the number in 'human friendly' base ten. We can vary this a little by using *%x*, which prints an *int* value in base sixteen (hexadecimal), or *%o* which prints it in base eight (octal). A simple example is:

```
int n;
n=249;
printf("%i is %x in hex. and %o in octal" ,n,n,n);
```

This results in a message on the screen reading:

```
249 is f9 in hex and 371 in octal
```

If we want to print out a value stored in a *float* variable we must use the format codes *%f*, which prints the value with a fixed number of decimal places (e.g. 0.00002), or *%e* which prints the number in scientific format (e.g. 2.3e+007 which reads '2 point 3 times ten to the power of 7'). There is also a *%g* code which results in the use of either of the *%f* or *%e* formats, depending on which is most appropriate.

Here is an example using these codes:

```
float x;
x=234.567;
printf("Fixed point: %f. Scientific: %e",x,x);
```

The resulting message displayed is:

Fixed point: 234.567000. Scientific: 2.345670e+002

It is a common mistake to use the wrong format codes for the wrong type of variable. We must only use *%i, %o* and *%x* for values which are of *int* type and *%f* and *%e* for values which are of *float* type. Consider the following program which multiplies an integer by a floating point value and displays the result (which will also be a floating point value).

```
#include <stdio.h>
main()
{
  int n=4;
  float result,x=1.2;

  result=n*x;
  printf("%i times %f is %f", n, x, result);
}
```

Notice that we have initialised the variables *x* and *n* to the values 1.2 and 4 at the same time as defining them. The resulting message is:

4 times 1.200000 is 4.800000

However, an easy mistake to make is to mix up the *%i* and *%f* in the *printf* format string, such as:

printf("%f times %i is %f", n, x, result);

The resulting output will be nonsense, because *printf* will initially see a *%f* and tries to interpret the first value in the list, which is the contents of the variable called *n*, as if it where a *float* type variable. As seen before, the format in which floating point and integer values are stored is totally different and so *printf* will misinterpret the bit pattern and end up printing unexpected values. A similar problem occurs when we reach the *%i* code, as *printf* interprets the bit pattern of variable called *x* as if it were an integer, even though it is defined as a *float*. The final *%f* results in the correct value of variable called *result* being printed since it is of *float* type. The resulting message is something like:

0.023453 times 67342 is 4.800000

Note that we have not corrupted any of the data in the variables. All that has happened is that the *printf* has read the values of some variables and has misinterpreted them.

There are other format codes available. In particular, there is *%c* for printing out a character value and *%s* for printing out a string value. Examples of these can be seen in later sections. In summary we have the following codes available.

For *int* type values we can use the following format codes:

%i	prints integer in decimal
%d	same as %i
%u	prints unsigned integer in decimal
%x	prints integer in hexadecimal
%o	prints integer in octal

For *long int* values all the above should be preceded by '*l*', e.g:

%li	prints long integer in decimal
%lo	prints long integer in octal

For *float* values we can use the following format codes:

%f	prints float as fixed point number
%e	prints in scientific format
%g	either of above (use whichever is shorter)

For *double* (i.e. long floating point) values the above are preceded by '*l*', e.g:

%le	prints long float in scientific format
%lf	prints out a long float in fixed format

For printing character or string values use:

%c	print character
%s	print string

7.5 Width and precision

When using *printf* you will notice that the space occupied by a value will vary according to the number of numerals required to print the value. For instance, if we execute the statement:

```
printf("The answers are %i and %i.",42,1230);
```

The resulting message printed is:

```
The answers are 42 and 1230.
```

When using the format code %i, *printf* always prints integers with a width as small as necessary to print the number correctly. This is usually fine, but if we are printing out a table of numbers, then each number must occupy the same space on the screen or else the columns will not line up. To force a number to be printed with a certain width we use a format code such as *%3i*. This means that the integer is printed with a width of three. If it is only a two-digit number then an extra space is added at the front. Consider the following example:

```
printf("The answer is %3i!!",42);
```

The resulting message (with an underscore to indicate the added space) is:

```
The answer is _42!!
```

If a value will not fit into the specified width (e.g. if we used *%3i* to print 5674) then the width is increased as necessary such that the number is properly displayed.

We can also control if the spaces used as padding are placed before or after the actual figures (i.e. whether the figures are right or left justified in the space available). By default *printf* will use right justification, but a negative width will mean that it uses left justification. Here are a few examples of codes used to print the value 2468 showing how spaces are added:

%i	2	4	6	8		
%3x	9	a	4			
%6i			2	4	6	8
%-6i	2	4	6	8		
%2i	2	4	6	8		

When printing out floating point values, we can specify the width as above (which includes space taken up by decimal point and exponent). However, we may also want to specify the precision to which we want the number printed by specifying how many decimal places to use (default is 6). For example, the format code *%10.2f* means print the value with a width of ten overall and to two decimal places. Here are a few examples of using this technique to print the value 46.139:

%f	4	6	.	1	3	9	0	0	0

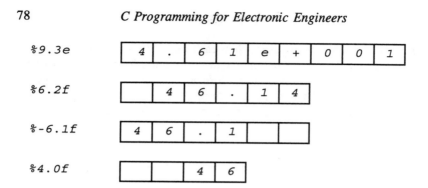

7.6 Escape sequences

Some ASCII codes do not have printable symbols associated with them but instead are control 'characters' which can affect the screen or printer to which they are sent. Because these characters do not have a printable symbol associated with them, we cannot type them directly into our program and there is no key for them on the keyboard. There are also symbols which have a special meaning to the C compiler. For example, if we wish to have a double quote in our *printf* format string as in this example we will have problems.

```
printf("Welcome to this "C" program.");
```

Since the double quote is used to mark the ends of a string the compiler becomes confused as to where the string begins and ends. To get around this problem C uses the idea of an escape sequence. This is where we use a special symbol (\) to tell the compiler that the next character does not have its usual meaning but is a non-printable character, or a printable character without its special meaning. Some of these sequences are listed below:

\n   Newline char. Move cursor to start of next line
\a   Bell character (makes computer bleep)
\b   Backspace (move cursor back one place)
\t   Tab character (moves cursor 8 spaces)
\v   Vertical tab (moves cursor down one place)
\"   Print a double quote
\'   Print a single quote
\\   Print a backslash

So, for our example above we will need to use the line:

```
printf("Welcome to this \"C\" program.");
```

which will print the message:

```
Welcome to this "C" program.
```

The escape sequence that is most often used is \n which starts a new line. Say we wanted to print the following message at the left-hand side of the screen:

```
Welcome!
Press any key to continue
```

It is tempting to use *printf* as follows to do this:

```
printf("Welcome!
Press any key to continue");
```

Although this might seem reasonable in principle, the compiler will complain because it does not allow you to have a string extending over more than one line. What we do instead is include the escape sequence for the new line character (i.e. \n) in the string. Instead of being printed, this character moves the cursor to the start of the next line. Our statement therefore becomes:

```
printf("Welcome!\nPress any key to continue");
```

Note that the next *printf* statement would start printing after the 'e' of the word 'continue'.

7.7 Self-assessment test — *printf*

Consider the program below. For each of the *printf* statements note how the output will appear for those statements that are valid.

```
main()
{
  int        n=3457;
  long int m=9876543;
  float      x=987.654;
  float      y=2e20;
  char       ch='G';

  printf("%i,     \n",n);    /* a */
  printf("%d,     \n",n);    /* b */
  printf("%-6d, \n",n);      /* c */
  printf("%i,     \n",m);    /* d */
  printf("%3li, \n",m);      /* e */
  printf("%x,     \n",n);    /* f */
  printf("%f,     \n",x);    /* g */
  printf("%8.2f, \n",x);     /* h */
  printf("%-6.1f,\n",x);     /* i */
  printf("%e,     \n",x);    /* j */
```

```
    printf("%8.1e,\n",x);    /* k */
    printf("%f,    \n",y);    /* l */
    printf("%e,    \n",y);    /* m */
    printf("%e,    \n",n);    /* n */
    printf("%c,    \n",ch);   /* o */

    printf("Answers are %i and %f.\n", n, x);/* p */
    printf("The result is:-\n%li.\a",m);     /* q */
}
```

Answers:

a) 3457, Printed 4 wide as necessary.   b) 3457,   %d is same as %i c) 3457__, Printed 6 wide, so padded with two spaces at end (left justified).   d) (??) Invalid! Using %li to print an integer. Will get totally unpredictable value. e) 9876543, Will not fit in width of 3, so minimum width necessary is used. f) d81, Printed in hex width minimum width necessary.   g) 987.653992, Printed to six decimal places. Note float only holds to accuracy of about 7 significant digits and so subsequent digits are unpredictable.   h)__987.65, Printed 8 wide (padded with two leading spaces) and to 2 decimal places.   i) 987.7_,   Printed 6 wide (left justified with one space). Rounding up of first decimal place. j) 9.876540e+002,   Printed in scientific format in minimum width necessary. k) 9.9e+002, Printed with one decimal place and width 8. l) 200000004008175500000.000000, Printed in minimum width with six decimal places. Note random nature of digits after about first eight (see g) for reason). m) 2.000000e+020,   Printed in minimum width scientific format with 6 decimal places.   n) -4.603485e+001, Invalid. Using %e to print an integer. Result unpredictable. o) G, Prints character in width of one. p) Answers are 3457 and 987.653992. Prints with values minimum width. q) The result is: (start of newline) 9876543. Prints with newline in middle and bleeps.

7.8 Input using *scanf*

The *scanf* function works in reverse to *printf*. A format string is used to describe the layout of the input and how to convert incoming 'human readable' values to bit representations appropriate for the variable type used to store the values. Following the format string, the addresses of variables in which values are stored are listed. A simple example is a program to read two integer numbers from the keyboard and display their sum:

```
#include <stdio.h>

main()
{
  int a,b;
```

```
    printf("Please enter two integer numbers:- \n");
    scanf("%i",&a);
    scanf("%i",&b);

    printf("\nThe sum of %i and %i is %i.",a,b,a+b);
}
```

This program first prints an appropriate message using *printf* and then reads a value from the keyboard using the first *scanf* statement. The first of the parameters for *scanf* is a string containing the format code %i. This code tells *scanf* to expect the user to type a number which will need to be converted to the bit pattern of an integer variable. The second parameter indicates where *scanf* should store the value once it has been read and converted to integer format. In this case, we want the value to be stored in the integer variable called *a*. Notice that we have prefixed the variable name with the '& ' symbol. Do not worry at this stage what this symbol means, but just accept that it must be there (in fact '&a' evaluates to the memory address of variable *a*). If it is left out, then the program will not read the value properly and may even cause the computer to crash! The second *scanf* statement will read another value entered by the user and store it in the variable called *b*. The *printf* statement then displays the result. An example of the output of this program is shown below, with the user's entries in bold:

```
please enter two integer numbers:
120
57
The sum of 120 and 57 is 177.
```

When the *scanf* function is executed, the user is not automatically prompted to enter a value, and the machine will simply sit quietly waiting for the user to type something and press the return key. Hence, when using *scanf* it is necessary to prompt the user to type something with a preceding *printf*, as in the program above.

If the program is to read in an integer and a floating point number and multiply them, then it would look like this:

```
#include <stdio.h>
main()
{
  int a;
  float x;
  printf("Input an integer");
  scanf("%i",&a);
  printf("Input a real number");
  scanf("%f",&x);
  printf("%i multiplied by %f is %f", a, x, a*x);
}
```

Notice that we must prompt the user very carefully here. We must ensure that the first number entered is an integer (e.g. 45 or 9). If the user were to enter a real number here (e.g. 3.4 or 4563.08), then *scanf* would notice that the value entered is not an integer and so give up, resulting in variable *a* maintaining its original value. What is worse is that no error message will occur and the program will just continue regardless. In the second *scanf* statement, we are reading in a floating point value, so we use the code %f to instruct *scanf* to convert the value to the bit pattern representation of a *float* type variable and save it in the variable called *x*. The user may enter real values (e.g. 4.56) or values which appear to be integers (e.g. 88). These will be successfully read and stored. If the value appears to be an integer it will be interpreted as the value with a point and a string of zeros following it (e.g. 88 is read as 88.000000).

We can use all the format codes, as in *printf* (%x, %c, %li, etc.), but we must ensure that the variable to receive the value is of the matching type to the format code.

7.9 Self-assessment test − *scanf*

Which of the following *scanf* statements are valid and what values are stored in the receiving variables?

```
#include <stdio.h>
main()
{
  int n;
  long int m;
  float x=0;
  char   ch;

  scanf("%i",&n);      /* a. user types "56"  */
  scanf("%i",&m);      /* b. user types "33"  */
  scanf("%x",&n);      /* c. user types "a3"  */
  scanf("%o",n);       /* d. user types "10"  */
  scanf("%i",&n);      /* e. user types "3.3" */

  scanf("%f",&x);      /* f. user types "0.6" */
  scanf("%f",&n);      /* g. user types "8"   */
}
```

Answers:

a) 56 is stored in variable *n*. b) Invalid. Using %i to read a *long int*. Should use %li. Value in *m* unpredictable. c) The value a3 (163 in decimal) is stored in variable *n*. d) Invalid. The value 10 octal (8 decimal) is read and converted to integer format successfully. However, because the *'&'* is missing before *'n'* then we do not know where the value is stored (it may overwrite other data or program as well!).   e) This is a valid *scanf* statement, but user has entered a non-integer value. The value *n* is left unchanged. Some or all of the input string will remain in the input buffer.   f) The value 0.6 is successfully placed in variable *x*. g) Invalid. We are using *%f* to read an *int*. The value placed in *n* will be unpredictable and also, because the *%f* code produces a result twice the size of an *int* variable, we will overwrite data or code next to *n* in memory.

7.10   Problems with *scanf*

The *scanf* function usually causes novice programmers numerous problems. This arises from several factors. Firstly, because *scanf* is an extremely flexible and powerful facility, it requires a good deal of practice to use it effectively. To overcome this we will stick to the most simple and basic usage possible.

Secondly, problems can arise because the compiler does not check for compatibility of variable type and format codes (e.g. using *%f* to read a value into an integer variable). The consequence of such an error is usually that the value entered is misinterpreted and so peculiar values are placed in the receiving variables.

The third source of problems is that *scanf* does not automatically tell the user if the value entered is invalid (e.g. user types "Hello" when *scanf* was expecting and integer number). Usually, under such circumstances *scanf* just gives up and the program ploughs on regardless, without informing the user of a problem.

To avoid such problems it is recommended that the following points are checked when using *scanf*.

Firstly, only read one value at a time even, if it means using many *scanf* statements to read a series of values. It is possible to read more than one value such as in the following section of program:

```
int n;
float x;
double l;
scanf("%i %f %lf",n,x,l);
```

This reads an integer into variable *n*, a real number into *x* and a real into *l* (note the use of *%lf* for *double* variables). A valid line of input from the user would be three numbers separated by spaces or carriage returns (N.B. the first value must be an integer):

```
45 6.7 9990.8
```

Because the format string in *scanf* contains spaces, these must occur in the input string. Therefore, we cannot enter the line delimited by any other character (except carriage return) such as commas:

```
45, 6.7, 9990.8
```

In this instance *scanf* would give up after reaching the first unexpected comma. If it is the intention that the user should enter the values separated by commas then the *scanf* statement should become:

```
scanf("%i,%f,%lf",&n,&x,&l);
```

which tells *scanf* to expect the commas. However, now the commas must be entered, or the same error occurs, with little or nothing being immediately evident when the program is running. To avoid such complications, it is suggested that the following method is used in this case:

```
scanf("%i",&n);
scanf("%f",&x);
scanf("%lf",&l);
```

The user can now simply enter three values, each with a carriage return.

Secondly, always check that the format code and the receiving variable are of compatible types. A common error of this kind is shown below:

```
int n;
scanf("%f",&n);
```

In this example we have instructed *scanf* to read in a value and convert it to the bit pattern representation used by a *float* type variable. We then copy this bit pattern into the variable called *n*. Now, since *n* is an integer variable and its representation of values is different to that of floating point variables, the bit pattern placed in *n* may represent a completely different value to the value entered by the user. What is worse is that a *float* value is twice the bit length of an integer, so we may well corrupt another variable or code located next to the variable *n* in memory. There are no error checks for this type of problem, so beware. The following is a summary of what codes to use with a given type of variable:

```
int         %i,%d,%o,%x
char        %c
float       %f
long int    %li,%ld,%lo,%lx
double      %lf
```

The third problem to look out for is when *scanf* receives input but cannot process it as requested. For example, if we have the statement:

```
scanf("%i",&n);
```

where *n* is an integer variable. This will work fine if the user enters 34 or 456, but *scanf* will not be able to process input such as 4.5, or "Boo", as these do not represent integer values. In these circumstances *scanf* will give up and not change the value in variable *n*. It will not be immediately obvious to the user that anything is wrong until it becomes apparent that the program is processing different values to those entered. This is a problem which can be countered, but for our purposes it is a shortcoming that we can live with for now.

7.11   Reading characters with *getchar*

When a single character is to be read (e.g. when the user responds by pressing a particular key) then the *getchar* function is useful. This can be done using *scanf*, but it is probably tidier using *getchar*, which is used as follows:

```
char reply;
reply=getchar();
```

When *getchar* is called the program waits until a key is pressed and then it returns a character value, which in this case is placed in the variable called *reply*.

A typical example of using *getchar* is to allow the user to select options by hitting certain keys. It is common to write programs such that the whole program can be re-run if the user wishes, or else the program ends. This is shown in the example below:

```
#include <stdio.h>
main()
{
  char reply;
  do
  {  .
     .
     (Body of program)
     .
     .
     printf("Hit Q to quit or other key to re-run");

     fflush(stdio);
     reply=getchar();
     reply=toupper(reply)
  }
  while (reply!='Q');
  printf("Program finished");
}
```

Notice the inclusion of the *stdio.h* header file which is needed when using *getchar*. At the end of the program we ask the user to indicate their choice by hitting a key. We read which key is hit by using *getchar* which places the character corresponding to the key in the character variable called *reply*. Since we do not know if the shift lock is on or off (i.e. hitting the key marked 'Q' can result in *getchar* returning 'Q' or 'q' which are different characters), we convert the character in the variable called *reply* to upper case using the function *toupper*. This returns its character argument converted to upper case if it is a lower case letter, or otherwise returns the value unchanged. At this point the value in *reply* is guaranteed to be upper case, so we can then terminate the program if it is a 'Q', or otherwise loop back using the *while* statement. The *fflush* statement is discussed later and is not vital to understanding the program.

7.12   Detecting key strokes

One feature of *getchar()* is that it suspends execution and waits for a key to be struck before the program execution continues. This is not suitable if we want a means of interrupting a running program by hitting a key. Consider a program in which the computer is turned into a clock that simply displays the time. This requires the machine to be constantly running the program. In order to make the program terminate, we need it to periodically test if a key has been hit without suspending execution. If no key was hit the program continues displaying the time or otherwise terminates. To do this we use the function *kbhit* (keyboard hit) which returns 0 if no key is hit or 1 if a key has been hit. This is shown in the outline example below:

```
/* Clock program to constantly display time */
#include <stdio.h>

main()
{
  do
  {
    (get time using standard routine)
    (if time has changed then redisplay time)
  }
  while (kbhit()==0);
}
```

This will allow us to keep looping through the program until a key is pressed. N.B. The *kbhit* function is not a standard function and may not be available on some compilers. On others it may have a different name or be used differently, so you will need to check the documentation with the compiler.

7.13   Keyboard buffering

Most computers use the concept of an input buffer for the keyboard. Having a buffer associated with the keyboard means that you can type ahead of a program which reads the keyboard. The characters typed are stored away in an area of memory (called a buffer) ready for when the program requires them. It is the operating system that actually communicates with the keyboard and places anything typed into the buffer. When our C programs require input they actually take characters from the buffer (or wait for input if the buffer is empty).

Although buffering is a useful technique, it can cause problems sometimes as things can get left in the buffer unexpectedly. Consequently, later input operations pick up these left-over characters instead of what we typed. This can happen when using *getchar* or *scanf* because we must type carriage return (on most systems) to initiate a response. Although the characters that we type are read out of the buffer the carriage return character can be left in the buffer. This is often not a problem if the next input operation is to read a numerical value (e.g. *scanf("%i", &n)*) because carriage returns are disregarded. However, if we are reading a character, then *scanf* or *getchar* will take the first character it finds in the buffer. Since the carriage return character is considered to be no different to any other then we can end up reading the carriage return from the tail end of the last input. If problems occur, the simple remedy is to ensure that the buffer is emptied before each input operation. This is done by calling the standard function called *fflush* which clears (flushes out) a specified buffer. For the keyboard, the buffer is identified as *stdin* and so to flush it we write:

```
fflush(stdin);
```

An example of this in use is shown later.

There may be other non-standard functions available for I/O and it is worth checking what your compiler has to offer. In particular, there may be a version of *getchar* which avoids buffering and reads the keyboard directly. This is often useful as it can allow users to press keys and see a result without having to hit the carriage return key. However, the details of this may differ from one machine and compiler to another.

7.14   Detecting invalid input

When using *scanf* to read numerical values it is possible that the user will enter something invalid. Consider an example in which we want to read the user's age in years (for some reason). Assuming the existence of an integer variable called *age*, we could simply write:

```
printf("Please enter your age in years");
scanf("%i",&age);
```

This is fine, but it would be better if the program could check that the input is reasonable (i.e. has user entered −10 or 500!). We can improve this section of code by asking the user to re-enter a value until it is reasonable (i.e. between 0 and 120). This can be achieved by looping around the *scanf* statement until the value entered is within the acceptable limits and only then continuing onwards through the rest of the program. Here is how this is done:

```
do
{
  printf("Please enter your age in years");
  scanf("%i",&age);
  if ((age<0) || (age>120))
  {
    printf("\a\n Invalid. \n");
    printf("Re-type your age in range 0-100.");
  }
}
while ((age<0) || (age>120));
```

This program will pick up and rectify errors caused by the user entering unreasonable numbers. If the user does enter an unreasonable value a message is displayed, the computer will bleep and the user can then retype a value. However, a different type of error can occur if the user were to enter a value for age such as 'ABC'. This is obviously not a valid integer value. In this case *scanf* will leave characters in the buffer and finish without assigning any value to the variable called *age*. What happens next depends on whatever value was initially in the variable *age*. If it happened to be between 0 and 120 then program will continue onwards with this value whatever it might be. If it is not in this range then we loop back to the *scanf* statement, but the buffer still contains 'ABC' and so the same thing happens and we end up continually travelling around the loop and there is nothing easy that the user can do to stop it!

We can get around this problem as follows. Firstly, we can make sure that the buffer is emptied before using *scanf* by using the *fflush* function. Also, *scanf* actually returns an integer value which tells us how many values it has successfully read and converted (in this case there is only one value for it to read). We can therefore use this value and test if it is one indicating that the user's input was a valid integer, or it is zero indicating that the user typed something like 'ABC' which cannot be converted to an *int* value. The complete and foolproof section of program is shown below:

```
int age,converted;
do
{
```

```
printf("Please enter your age in years");
fflush(stdin);
converted=scanf("%i",&age);
if ((age<0) || (age>120) || (converted!=1))
{
  printf("\a \n Invalid.\n");
  printf("Re-type your age in range 0-100.");
}
}
while (age<0 || age>120 || converted!=0);
```

This is very similar to what we had before, but we have included the *fflush* function and also assigned the value returned by *scanf* to the integer variable called *converted*. We can then test the value of the variable *converted* to ensure that the user typed in a valid integer value.

7.15 Case study — Diode table

A program is required to print a table of values of diode currents for a series of different temperatures and forward voltages across the diode as shown:

```
Diode Current Verses Voltage and Temperature
```

Voltage	Temperature (Celsius)			
	-20	0	20	40
0.00	0.00e+000	0.00e+000	0.00e+000	0.00e+000
0.05	8.92e-014	7.38e-014	6.25e-014	5.39e-014
0.10	9.74e-013	6.93e-013	5.16e-013	3.98e-013
0.15	9.75e-012	5.88e-012	3.80e-012	2.60e-012
0.20	9.68e-011	4.94e-011	2.76e-011	1.67e-011
0.25	9.60e-010	4.14e-010	2.00e-010	1.06e-010
0.30	9.52e-009	3.47e-009	1.45e-009	6.80e-010
0.35	9.44e-008	2.91e-008	1.05e-008	4.34e-009
0.40	9.36e-007	2.44e-007	7.64e-008	2.78e-008
0.45	9.29e-006	2.05e-006	5.54e-007	1.77e-007
0.50	9.21e-005	1.72e-005	4.02e-006	1.13e-006
0.55	9.14e-004	1.44e-004	2.91e-005	7.24e-006
0.60	9.06e-003	1.21e-003	2.11e-004	4.62e-005
0.65	8.99e-002	1.01e-002	1.53e-003	2.95e-004
0.70	8.91e-001	8.47e-002	1.11e-002	1.89e-003

The diode equation is as follows:

$$I_f = I_r\left(e^{\frac{qV}{kt}} - 1\right)$$

where q is the charge on an electron and k is Boltzmann's constant. The value of I_r, which is the diode's reverse leakage current, is to be supplied by the user when the program runs. The values of V and t will change as the table is printed. The values of V are to go from 0 to 0.7 V in fourteen 0.05 V steps and the value of t is to go from -20 to 40 degrees Celsius (293 to 131 kelvin) in three 20° steps.

The initial directives and definitions will appear as follows:

```
#include <stdio.h>
#include <math.h>
#define K  1.3800662e-23   /* Boltzmann's const */
#define Q  1.6021892e-19   /* Electronic charge */
```

Here we include the header files *stdio.h* (for I/O functions) and *math.h* (for exponential function). We then define the constants K and Q appropriately and then define various variables as required. Notice that we use *double* type variables as opposed to *float* type, because the exponential function *exp* works with *double* type.

```
double t,V,If,Ir; /* temp, frwrd voltage frwrd */
                  /* current,revrs leak. current*/
int column,row;   /* counts columns and rows of */
                  /* table */
int    n;         /* other general use */
```

Around the complete program we have a large *do-while* loop to allow us to re-run the program without it terminating. The form of this loop is as follows:

```
do
{   .
    .
  (body of program)
    .
    .
  printf("\nPress Space to re-run");
  printf("\nPress any other key to exit");
  fflush(stdin);
}
while (getchar()==' ');
```

At the end of the program we use *getchar* to read a character from the keyboard and we test if it is a space. If it is a space, we loop back, otherwise we just continue to the end of the program. Since *getchar* is reading characters from the input buffer, it is as well to ensure that the buffer is empty first. It is quite possible that there are characters left (such a carriage returns) from the previous input operation which we do not want. By emptying the buffer using *fflush*, *getchar* is forced to wait for us to hit a key.

The main body of the program starts by reading the value of the reverse leakage current of the diode from the user. The following section of code allows us to do this and to check that the value is valid and reasonable:

```
printf("Enter Reverse leakage current of diode:");
do
{
  fflush(stdin);
  n=scanf("%lf",&Ir);

  /* Check value entered is valid & reasonable */
  if ((n!=1) || (Ir<0) || (Ir>1)) .
  {
    printf("\n\aInvalid!!. ");
    printf("\nEnter value between 0 and 1");
  }
}
while ((n!=1) || (Ir<0) || (Ir>1));
```

This section first prompts user to enter a value. Then inside a *do-while* loop we read the value using *scanf* (note that *%lf* is used for reading a *double* type value). We also note the integer value returned by *scanf* which indicates how many values it successfully converted. We now need to check what has happened. Firstly, we check that the variable *n* contains 1 indicating that the user has entered a recognisable number. If this is the case then we also want to ensure that the value is reasonable. The reverse leakage current of a diode is commonly pico or microamps. If the value is negative it is clearly unreasonable and if it is too big it will cause overflows. We therefore require it to be between 0 and 1 amp which should allow for most diodes! The *if* statement tests these criteria and prints an appropriate message (with a bleep from the \a) if anything is wrong. We then decide if we must loop back using the same test in the *while* statement.

Next we start to print the table. First, we print the headings as follows:

```
printf("\nDiode Current V. Voltage and Temp. ");
printf("\n\n Voltage      Temperature (Celsius) ");
printf("\n          -20      0      20      40\n");
```

Notice the widespread use of \n to start a new line and \n\n to introduce a complete blank line. To get the headings lined up nicely when they are printed usually requires much trial and error. We now need to print out each row of the table, which requires a loop that runs fifteen times, once for each row. Each time around the loop we must begin a new line for the row and calculate and print the corresponding voltage for that row. The voltage (*V*) is calculated by multiplying 0.05 by the number of rows that we have printed. We must then print each of the four values of current in that row. The outline layout is then:

```
for (row=0;row<=14;row++)
{
  V=0.05*row;
  printf("\n%4.2f      ",V);

  (print each column across line)

}
```

To print each of the four columns of the row we use another *for* loop. For each column we must calculate the corresponding temperature (the formula *20*column−20* gives values of −20, 0, 20 and 40 for *column* equal to 0, 1, 2 and 3). We then convert the temperature to kelvin by adding 273. We now have all the values required to calculate the forward diode current so, using the diode equation, we evaluate I_f and print it. Notice that the current is printed with a set width to keep the table straight and we do not have a \n in the format string, so each will follow directly after the previous value printed on the same line.

```
for (column=0;column<=3;column++)
{
  t=20*column-20;
  t=t+273;

  If=Ir*(exp((Q*V)/(K*t))-1);
  printf("%9.2e    ",If);
}
```

The complete program is as follows:

```
/* Program to print current through a diode at a*/
/* series of different forward voltages. The     */
/* currents at temperatures  of -20 0 20 and 40 */
/* celsius are displayed in different columns    */

#include <stdio.h>
#include <math.h>

#define K   1.3800662e-23    /* Boltzmann's const */
#define Q   1.6021892e-19    /* Electronic charge */

main()
{
  double t,V,If,Ir; /* temp, frwd.V, frwd.I, */
                    /* rvrse lkge I          */
  int column, row;  /* counts cols. and      */
                    /*rows of table       */
  int n;            /* other general use     */

  /* Loop around whole program to */
  /* allow re-run if desired      */
```

```
do
{
  /* Read in reverse leakage current */
  /* and store in Ir                 */
  printf("Enter Reverse leakage current:");
  do
  {
    fflush(stdin);
    n=scanf("%lf",&Ir);

    /* Check value entered is valid  */
    /* and reasonable                */
    if ((n!=1) || (Ir<0) || (Ir>1))
    {
      printf("\n\aInvlid!!.");
      printf("Enter value between 0 and 1");
    }
  }
  while ((n!=1)||(Ir<0)||(Ir>1));
  /* Loop back if necessary */

  /* Value of Ir now read. Now print */
  /* heading of table                */

  printf("\nDiode Current V Voltage & Temp.");
  printf("\n\nVoltage   Celsius(Celsius)");
  printf("\n   -20     0     20       40\n");

  /* Heading complete.Now use loop to */
  /* print each row. Require 15 rows   */
  /* corresponding to inc. of 0.05V    */

  for (row=0;row<=14;row++)
  {
    /* Calculate frwd voltage for row */
    /* and print it at start of line  */
    V=0.05*row;
    printf("\n%4.2f      ",V);

    /* Now loop for each column in row */
    /* and print values of current     */
    for (column=0;column<=3;column++)
    {
      /* Calculate temp. for this row */
      t=20*column-20;
      t=t+273;   /* convert to kelvin */
      /* Calc If using diode equtn */
      /* and print                 */
      If=Ir*(exp((Q*V)/(K*t))-1);
      printf("%9.2e    ",If);
    }
  }
}
```

```
      /* Table done, ask if they want to quit */
      printf("\nPress space to re-run.");
      printf("\nPress any other key to exit");
      fflush(stdin);
   }
   while (getchar()==' ');
}
```

7.16   Summary

● *printf* is the prime means of outputting text to the monitor. The form of the output is specified in a format string which is followed by any values to be substituted to form the output string.

● *scanf* is primarily the means of reading values from the keyboard. In a simple mode of usage a format string indicates the type of internal representation to which the value entered is to be converted. This is followed by the address of the variable to receive the value.

● Input from keyboards is often buffered. The *fflush* function can be used to empty the buffer.

● Usually there are non-standard functions available with different compilers for tasks such as reading keys directly or detecting key hits. This is usually something worth investigating.

7.17   Exercises

1) Correct the errors in the following program which reads in the two shorter sides of a right-angled triangle and prints the length of the hypotenuse using Pythagoras's theorem.

```
#include <stdio.h>
#include <math.h>


main()
{
   double SideA,SideB,Hypot;

   printf(Please enter length of first side);
   scanf("%f",&SideA);
   printf("Please enter length of second side");
   scanf("%lf",SideB);
```

```
Hypot=sqrt(SideA*SideA+SideB*SideB);

printf("/n/n");
printf("The hypotenuse of a triangle with sides
       of %lf and %lf is %lf",Hypot, SideA, SideB);
}
```

2) Write a program to print times tables up to 10 as follows:

```
 1    2    3    4    5    6    7    8    9   10
 2    4    6    8   10   12   14   16   18   20
 3    6    9   12   15   18   21   24   27   30
 4    8   12   16   20   24   28   32   36   40
 5   10   15   20   25   30   35   40   45   50
 6   12   18   24   30   36   42   48   54   60
 7   14   21   28   35   42   49   56   63   70
 8   16   24   32   40   48   56   64   72   80
 9   18   27   36   45   54   63   72   81   90
10   20   30   40   50   60   70   80   90  100
```

Modify the program so that instead of going up to ten it will first prompt the user for the size of the required table.

3) Write a program to read in ten integer numbers and print their mean. This will require a loop (do not use ten *scanf* statements!). Each time around the loop the value entered can be added to a running total. Once the program is running make it error proof so that if users type something like "Yippee", or if they enter a value that is not between −32000 and +32000, then they are asked to re-enter another value.

8 Functions

8.1 Introduction

The use of functions is a fundamental feature of C programming. Their use makes programming a more logically structured task, more efficient in the amount of source code required and helps to make the task of making subsequent changes to the program easier. We have already used some functions which are prewritten and supplied in library files (e.g. *printf* and *exp*). However, the libraries cannot contain every conceivable function we might ever require and so we will cover in this chapter how to write 'customised' functions.

8.2 Simple procedural functions

The simplest form of a function is a block of code which has an associated identifier. This block of code is written separately from our *main* section of the program. When writing the complete program we can then call this function by quoting its identifier. This means that the whole block of code is executed at any point where its identifier is placed. The general form of a simple function is as follows:

```
void function_identifier(void)
{
  local_variable_definitions;
  statement;
  statement;
     .
     .
  statement;
}
```

The function starts with the word *void* indicating that this is a simple function which does not return a value (more on this later). Then follows a function identifier, which is a name that is associated with the function, and then the word *void* in brackets. Then the body of the function follows inside *{}* symbols. The body of the function is essentially a mini C program which is exactly the same in form as all the programs we have seen previously. It starts with variable definitions (called local variables) and then a sequence of C statements. A simple example of such a function is one to clear the screen on a PC type machine. This can be achieved in a crude manner by sending lots of newline characters to the monitor, causing anything on the screen to scroll off the top. Here is a function to achieve this:

```
void clear_screen(void)
{
  int n;
  for (n=1;n<=25;n++)
  {
    printf("\n");
  }
}
```

What we have written is called a function definition and this will generally appear after the end of our *main* program. We have defined a function called *clear_screen* which when executed will send 25 newline characters to the monitor using *printf*. However, this function will not be executed until it is called. This means that its name must be quoted in the *main* program or inside another function. Therefore, our *main* program may look like this:

```
main()
{
  clear_screen();
  printf("Hello world");
}
```

When executed this will first call the *clear_screen* function (the empty brackets must be included in the call). The *clear_screen* function will then execute and cause the screen to become blank. Once finished the flow of execution returns the *main* program to the next statement after the call. This is a *printf* statement and we therefore get the message 'Hello World' printed on an otherwise empty screen.

8.3 Parameterised functions

Most functions are more general purpose than the one we have illustrated above. Usually functions require some values on which their operation depends and so we must provide the function with values (called arguments) when it is called. For example, a function to calculate cosines will require that we supply the value of an angle for which we want to know the cosine. The general form of a definition of this type of function is

```
void function_identifier(parameter_list)
{
  local_variable_definition
  statement;
  statement;
    .
    .
}
```

The only difference here from the previous section is the inclusion of the parameter list, which defines what types of values the function is passed when called and the variables in which these values are held. Consider a function which calculates and prints the area of a triangle when supplied with the dimensions of the base and height. The function definition will appear as follows:

```
void tri_area(float base, float height)
{
  float area;

  area=base*height/2;
  printf("\n Area is %f",area);
}
```

When called we must now provide two *float* type values that are copied into the variables *base* and *height* (both of type *float*) which are then used in the function to calculate the area. A third variable is used in the function called *area* but, unlike the other two, its value is not known at the start of the execution of the function. To call this function we might have the following line in our *main* program:

```
tri_area(1.2,3.4);
```

This calls the function and copies the values 1.2 into variable *base* and 3.4 into the variable *height*, before execution of the function commences. The result of this call is the message:

```
Area is 2.040000
```

The advantage of using functions is that they tidy up blocks of code into logical units which perform a well-defined task. Also, we can use a function as many times as we like within a program. For instance, we can write:

```
tri_area(3.4,6.7);
tri_area(4.5,8.9);
tri_area(9.0,8.8);
```

This results in the function being called three times with different arguments and so the following will appear on the monitor:

```
Area is 11.390000
Area is 20.250000
Area is 39.600000
```

We can have as many parameters as we like in our functions, simply by listing them inside the brackets after the function identifier. Each parameter definition consists of the type of the parameter (e.g. *float, int*) followed by the identifier of the variable which will hold the value that is passed from the call. Parameter definitions are separated by commas. The call must contain the corresponding number of arguments of an appropriate type. The arguments are copied to the parameter variables in the order in which the parameters are defined. If a function requires no parameters then the word *void* is placed inside the brackets.

8.4 Self-assessment test — Functions

Here is a function which calculates and prints the value of a real number base to the power of and integer index (e.g. 6.7^4 or 0.78^2). The function works by multiplying the base by itself a number of times according to the index (e.g. 6.7^4 is calculated as 6.7*6.7*6.7*6.7).

```
void power(float base, int index)
{
  float x;
  int n;

  x=1;
  /* Following loop executes `index` times */
  for (n=1;n<=index;n++)
  {
    x=x*base;
  }
  printf("%5.2f to power of %i is %5.2f"
      ,base,index,x);
}
```

Which of the following are valid calls and, if valid, what is printed?

a) *power(7.8);*   b) *power(4.0,3);*   c) *Power(3.0,5);*
d) *power (2.5,3.3);* e) *power(7.8,0);*   f) *power(4.4,-7);*

Answers: a) Invalid. This function requires two arguments.   b) Valid. Message printed is '4.00 to power of 3 is 64.00'.   c) Invalid. C is case sensitive so *Power* and *power* are seen as different.   d) Valid. Second argument will be converted to an *int* when passed to function, so result is $2^3 = 8$. e) Valid. Will raise 7.8 to the power of zero, so result is 1.   f) A valid call but will get wrong result. 4.4^{-7} is equal to 31.32×10^{-6} but the *for* loop cannot go around −7 times! Instead, the *for* loop will not execute at all, so result will be 1. This is a limitation of the function in that it cannot deal with negative indices.

8.5 Functions with return values

Many functions are written such that they return a value to the point where the function was called. We have already seen examples of such functions, such as the *cos, sqrt* and *time* functions, which all perform some calculation and return a value. Such functions are not called in the same manner as in the previous examples but instead usually form part of an expression. For example:

```
x=2*cos(0.5);
```

When executed, this statement needs to calculate a value to assign to variable *x*, but when evaluating the expression a reference to the *cos* function is encountered. At this point the *cos* function (which is available from the standard libraries) is called and is passed the argument 0.5. This function then performs the necessary calculations to find the appropriate result, which is then returned when the function finishes and is used in completing the evaluation of the original expression.

The general form of definition of this type of function is as follows:

```
return_type     function_identifer(parameter_def.)
{
  local_variable_definitions;
  statement;
  statement;
     .
     .
  return return_value;
}
```

This differs from the previous examples of function definitions in that the initial word *void* is replaced with the type of the value which the function returns (e.g. *int, double, char*). Also, there must be at least one *return* statement within the function which indicates what value will be passed back to the point where the function was called. A simple example is a function to calculate the square of a *float* type value.

```
float square(float x)
{
  float result;

  result=x*x;
  return result;
}
```

The first line specifies that this function is called *square* and expects a single argument which will be stored in the *float* type variable *x*. The leading word *float* also indicates that this function will return a *float* type value when it completes execution. To call this function we might write:

```
y=square(5.4);
```

This calls the function passing the argument 5.4 to variable *x*. This square of *x* is then calculated and stored in the variable *result*. The final statement is a *return* statement which causes the function to end and also passes back the value of the expression that follows it. In this case it returns the contents of the variable *result* which will be 29.16. Therefore, the variable *y* will be assigned the value 29.16.

Consider another example concerned with charging and discharging a capacitor through a resistance. We will get the familiar exponential voltage curves shown in Figure 8.1, where V_{start} is the initial capacitor voltage, V_{aim} is the final capacitor voltage after infinite time, and V(t) is the capacitor voltage at a particular time t.

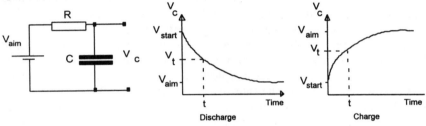

Figure 8.1 Charging and discharging curves

The general equation for calculating V(t) at a given time t is

$$V(t) = V_{aim} + \left(V_{start} - V_{aim}\right).e^{\frac{-t}{RC}}$$

Note that this equation will work for charging and discharging and is much more useful than the two separate equations usually given, which also assume an initial or final voltage of 0. A function to evaluate this equation will require five arguments (V_{aim}, V_{start}, R, C and t) and would be defined as follows:

```
float cap_voltage(float Vaim, float Vstart,
                  float R, float C, float t)
{
  float Vt;

  Vt=Vaim+(Vstart-Vaim)*exp((-t)/(R*C));
  return Vt;
}
```

Notice the use of the standard function *exp*. It is perfectly legitimate to call a function from within another function. A call to this function may take the form:

```
x=cap_voltage(5.0, 1.5, 1000.0, 1.0e-6, 0.0001);
```

Functions which return values must end execution at a *return* statement. There may be several *return* statements within a function allowing the function to terminate at several points. If such a function can terminate by reaching its last statement without executing a *return* statement, then the program will terminate with an error message.

8.6 Function prototypes

When writing a program we will have function definitions and also calls to these functions. On compiling the program, the compiler will check that each call to a function has the correct number of arguments, and examine the type of the arguments and return value to see if any type conversions are necessary. To do this the compiler must first have encountered the function definition to know this information. This may not be the case because our chosen layout may dictate that the definitions appear after the calls or, if two functions call each other (called mutual recursion), it is impossible to arrange all function definitions before their calls. Consequently, a method is supplied whereby we can forewarn the compiler of the existence of a function definition along with any information that it requires regarding the return value and parameters of the function. This is done using a function prototype which, if placed near the beginning of our source code files, will prevent any errors occurring due to the compiler encountering calls to functions that it does not yet know anything about. A function prototype is a copy of the first line of the function definition terminated with a semicolon. For the earlier example of the function for calculating the square of a value (section 8.5) the function prototype will be:

```
float square(float x);
```

Function prototypes are not always strictly necessary if we lay the program out in a particular fashion, but to minimise problems and maintain consistency we will use function prototypes for all the functions that we write. One point worth mentioning is how the compiler knows about the form of standard library functions, such as *exp*, since we do not supply a function prototype. This is achieved by using the *#include* directive to include in our program the header file *math.h*. This header file actually contains the function prototype for the *exp* and all other standard mathematical functions. Therefore, this file must be included whenever using such a function, otherwise the compiler will complain.

Other standard library functions will require the inclusion of other header files.

The function prototype and the subsequent function definition must match, otherwise the compiler will flag an error.

8.7 Case study – Oscillator design table

The circuit of Figure 8.2 is a standard circuit for a Schmitt trigger signal generator. The opamp, R1 and R2 form a Schmitt trigger (hysteric comparator) with thresholds symmetric around zero (e.g. ± 2 V).

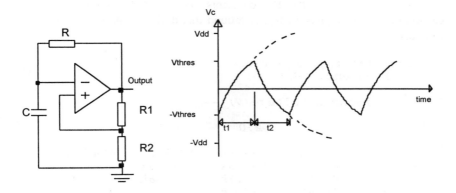

Figure 8.2 Schmitt trigger oscillator

The threshold voltages are calculated using the formula:

$$V_{thres} = \pm \frac{R_1}{R_1 + R_2} . V_{dd}$$

The output of the Schmitt trigger is fed back to the input but, since it is inverting, the circuit is unstable and will oscillate. We can control the frequency of oscillation by incorporating C and R in the feedback loop which slows down the rate at which the output affects the input. The result is that the capacitor is charged up and down through R between the thresholds of the Schmitt trigger as shown. Assuming that the power rails are symmetrical, the time of one of the exponential half cycles can be calculated using the equation of section 8.5 rearranged in the form:

$$t = -RC \ln \left[\frac{V_t - V_{start}}{V_{aim} - V_{start}} \right]$$

The frequency of oscillation is then found from:

$$f = \frac{1}{2t}$$

We desire a program to print out a design table so that the value of the threshold voltages and the RC constants can be obtained quickly without calculation for a frequency roughly around that desired. The table should look like this:

```
       Oscillator Design Table
          Frequency (Hz)

RC         Threshold Voltage(V)  -->
 |
 |          1.0        2.0        3.0        4.0

1.0e-006   455.1k     893.5k    1738.0k    4245.1k
3.2e-006   143.9k     282.5k     549.6k    1342.4k
1.0e-005    45.5k      89.3k     173.8k     424.5k
3.2e-005    14.4k      28.3k      55.0k     134.2k
1.0e-004     4.6k       8.9k      17.4k      42.5k
3.2e-004     1.4k       2.8k       5.5k      13.4k
1.0e-003     0.5k       0.9k       1.7k       4.2k
3.2e-003     0.1k       0.3k       0.5k       1.3k
```

The values of the RC constant are at the start of each row and the threshold voltage at the head of each column. The complete program is as follows:

```
/* Program to print design table for */
/* Schmitt trigger Oscillator        */

#include <stdio.h>
#include <math.h>

#define vdd       5.0       /* Power supply rails */
#define RC_start 1.0e-6     /* 1st RC value in table*/
#define RC_inc   sqrt(10)   /*increase in RC per row*/
#define rows      8         /* NO. of rows in table */
#define thr_start 1.0       /* First thres. value */
#define thr_inc   1.0       /* Increment per column */
#define columns   4         /* Columns in table */
```

```
/* Function Prototypes */
void print_table(void);
void print_header(void);
void print_header(void);
double charge_time(double Vstart, double Vaim,double
                    Vt, double RC);

/************************************************/

main()
{
  print_header();
  print_table();
}
/************************************************/
/* Print heading for table                    */

void print_header(void)
{
  int n;
  double thres;

  printf("\n\n\n\t\tOscillator Design Table.");
  printf("\n\t\t    Frequency (Hz)");
  printf("\n\nRC       Threshold Voltage(V)");
  printf(" -->\n|\n|\t    ");

  /* print values of RC across top of table */
  thres=thr_start;
  for (n=1;n<=columns;n++)
  {
    printf("%-8.1lf  ",thres);
    thres=thres+thr_inc;
  }
  printf("\n");
}
/************************************************/
/* Prints body of table                        */

void print_table(void)
{
  int row,col;          /*Counters of rows and columns*/
  double rc,thres;      /*Current value of RC & thres*/
  double t;             /*Calculated period cycle*/
  double freq;          /*Calculated freq  */

  rc=RC_start;
  for (row=1;row<=rows;row++)
  {
    printf("\n%-7.1le ",rc);
    thres=thr_start;
```

```
   for (col=1;col<=columns;col++)
   {
     /* Calculate time of each half of cycle */
     /* and hence the freq. and duty cycle   */
     t=2*charge_time(-thres,vdd,+thres,rc);
     freq=1/t;

     printf("%8.1lfk ",freq/1000);
     thres=thres+thr_inc;
   }
  rc=rc*RC_inc;
  }
}
/************************************************/
/* Calculate half cycle period                 */

double charge_time(double Vstart, double Vaim,
            double Vt, double RC)
{
  return -RC*log((Vt-Vstart)/(Vaim-Vstart));
}
```

The program begins with a sequence of *#define* directives which define a number of constants that determine the size and values in the table. These control the number of rows and columns in the table, the initial values in the table of the RC constant, and the threshold voltage and the increments to the values of each row and column across and down the table and the power rails (which roughly represent the output saturation levels of the opamp). Note that the threshold and power supply voltages are assumed to be symmetrical about ground. Defining all these constants here makes it easy to change them if a slightly different table is required, and avoids having to search through the program changing all occurrences of these values.

Next follows the function prototype of the four functions that we have written later on. These allow the compiler to be forewarned of their existence even though it has not encountered the function definitions at this point. The function prototypes are exact copies of the first line of the function definitions.

The *main* program is now very simple because all the work is done in separate functions. We first call the *print_header* function which prints out the title and the values of the threshold voltage which head each column. When this function has finished we return to the *main* program which then calls the *print_table* function. This essentially consists of two nested loops. The first loop prints each row of the table. It starts by printing at the start of a line the value of *rc* and then initiates a second loop to print each of the entries along the line. This means that each time around this loop the period of a half cycle is calculated by passing the various values to the *charge_time* function which returns a value from which the frequency is calculated. For each iteration of this loop the value used for the threshold voltage is incremented by adding an amount equal to *thr_inc*. After the last entry in the row is printed, the inner loop terminates and we reiterate back around the outer loop, causing the next row to be printed in a similar manner.

As we print each row, we use the \n code in *printf* to start a new line and we must also increase the value of the RC constant used in the calculation. Notice that this is a logarithmic scale, as opposed to a linear scale used for the threshold voltage. To achieve a log scale of 1, 10, 100, 1000... we would simply multiply the previous value of *rc* by ten. However, to subdivide these intervals for more detail we can multiply by the square root of 10 to achieve the values as shown. Hence the identifier *rc_inc* is substituted by the preprocessor with the text *sqrt(10)*, which is a call to the square root function.

8.8 Local variables

In the examples so far given we have variable definitions inside each function. These variables are known as local variables because they are only recognised within the function in which they are defined. In fact, these variables will only exist in memory for as long as a function is executing and their values are lost as the function terminates. Parameter definitions also create local variables, but these differ in that they are preloaded with values from the arguments of the function call when the function begins execution. In general, whenever a variable is defined with a block of code between *{}* symbols it is only recognised within this block of code. Any reference to the variable outside this area will cause a compiler error.

The concept of limiting the area in which a variable is known (called the scope of the variable) is good, in that it 'protects' the variables within a function from any outside influence. In a large software project where many people are writing self-contained functions, it would be disastrous if when the complete system was running one programmer's function unexpectedly modified a variable in another programmer's function just because they happened to have the same identifier.

A simple example of how this works is shown below.

```
main()
{
  int n;

  n=6;
  fred();
  printf("%i",n);
}

void fred(void)
{
  int n;
  n=7;
```

```
  printf("%i ",n);
}
```

The *main* part of the program has a local variable called *n* which is initially set to 6. The function *fred* is called which also has a local variable called *n*. However, this is a totally separate variable even though it has the same identifier as the variable defined in the *main* section. This new variable is initially set to 7 and then its value is printed. This function then terminates and control returns to the *main* program where we print the value of variable *n* which is local to this section, so we finally have printed:

```
7  6
```

Therefore, the variables in each function are totally isolated even though they might share the same identifiers. Remember that any variables used to receive parameters are treated in exactly the same fashion.

8.9 Global variables

It is possible to set up variables which are accessible at any point in an entire program. These are called global variables and they are created by placing a variable definition outside any area of the program between {} symbols. It is usual to place these definitions near the top of the file. Because global variables can be modified by any function, it means that it can be difficult to keep track of what may happen to the variable as the program progresses. Consequently, the use of global variables should be avoided if possible. A simple example to demonstrate how they work is shown below:

```
int g;

main()
{
  g=1;
  fred();
  printf("%i",g);
  bill();
  printf("%i",g);
}

void fred(void)
{
  g=2;
}

void bill(void)
{
```

```
    int g;
    g=3;
}
```

In this program we have defined a global integer variable called *g* outside of any *{}* symbols. In the main program we set this global variable to 1 and then call the function *fred*. This function has none of its own local variables, but can still access the global *g* and sets it to 2. On return to the main program we therefore print the value of the global *g* as 2. Next we call the function *bill*, which has a local variable defined also called *g*. This function then sets variable *g* to 3, but there is an ambiguity here because this function has access to the global variable called *g* and its own local variable called *g*. By convention, the compiler will always choose the local variable in this situation. On return to the main program we again print the value of the global *g* which will still have the value 2 which is then printed. The local variable contained in function *bill* will have ceased to exist when *bill* terminated execution.

Global variables will exist in memory during the entire duration of program execution. When global variables are defined, they will only be recognised in the program after the point at which they are defined. Therefore, they are usually defined near the top of the source file rather than at the end.

8.10   The *main* function

It may already have become apparent that the section of our programs between the *{}* symbols following the word *main* is in fact a function, defined exactly as we have described for any other function. The only difference is that this is always the first function to be executed. The definition of *main* does not usually have a return type specified, but if we wished we could write:

```
void main(void)
{
    .
    .
    .
}
```

The absence of the leading *void* or any other type identifier in a function definition will always result in the compiler assuming that the function returns an *int* type value. In the case of the *main* function there is nothing to pass this a value back to, but in some systems the operating system may use a returned value on termination of the program for some purpose. The *void* indicates that we have no parameters is optional, but we have used it elsewhere consistently. Again, in some systems the operating system can pass a value to the program on execution, through parameters defined in the *main* function.

8.11   Self-assessment test − Variable scope

For the following program describe what value is printed by each *printf* statement:

```
#include <stdio.h>

/* Function prototypes */
void first_func(void);
void second_func(void);
int third_func(int VarB);

/* Global definitions */
int varA,varB;

main()
{
  int varB,varC;

  varA=1;
  varB=2;
  varC=3;

  first_func();
  printf("%i ",varA);
  second_func();
  printf("%i ",varB);
  varC=third_func(varC);
  printf("%i ",varC);
}

void first_func(void)
{
  varA=8;
}

void second_func(void)
{
  varB=varA;
}

int third_func(int varA)
{
  int varD;
  varD=2*varA;
  return varD;
}
```

Answers: The function *first_func* simply sets the global variable *varA* to 8 which is then printed by the first *printf* statement. The function *second_func* sets the global *varB* equal to *varA* which contains 8. However, on return to the *main* function the second *printf* statement will print the value of a second *varB* variable which is local to *main* in preference to the global *varB*. The local *varB* variable was set to 2 near the start of *main*, so the value 2 is printed. On calling the *third_func* we pass as an argument the contents of *varC* which is 3. This value is copied to a variable local to *third_func* called *varA*. This local will be used in preference to the global *varA* throughout this function. A local variable *varD* is also created and is assigned a value equal to twice *varA* which will be 6. The value of *varD* is then passed back to the expression in which the function was called. Therefore, the value of *varC* in the *main* function becomes 6 and this is then printed. The final output is therefore:

```
8  2  6
```

8.12 Summary

- Functions allow sections of code to be assigned an identifier by which the whole section of code can then be 'called' from any other point in a program.

- Functions allow a section of code to be reused many times within a program. They also make programming easier by allowing the creation of self-contained 'units' of program, each of which performs a well-defined task.

- Functions can be passed arguments which are values that affect the behaviour of the function, or which the function can process. The values of the arguments are copied to receiving variables local to the function, which are called parameters.

- Functions can either perform some task and then terminate without returning a value, or they can return a single value which results from its execution. Functions with no return value are usually called simply by quoting their name, while functions which return a value are usually called during the evaluation of an expression.

- Since the compiler does not look ahead when compiling it can encounter a function call before the function definition is encountered, resulting in the compiler having insufficient information to continue. The use of function prototypes can be used to inform the compiler of the existence and nature of a function early on, in order to prevent this problem.

- Any variable defined within a function is said to be local and is not known outside the function in which the definition occurs. If a local variable has the same identifier as a global variable, then the local variable is used in preference. Local variables only exist in memory whilst the function they belong to is executing.

- A variable defined outside any function is called a global variable and can be referenced in all areas of the program. Global variables stay in existence for the entire period of execution of the program. Global variables make programs more complex and unpredictable, so local variables should be used in preference where possible.

8.13   Exercises

1) Write a program incorporating the function of section 8.4 which reads a floating point number and an integer number from the user. The program should print the floating point value raised to the power of the integer number. Adapt the program so that it will work correctly for positive and negative indices. This should only involve the addition of an *if* statement to the function *power*.

2) Write a program to calculate the square root of a real number. Do not use the standard library function to do this, but instead implement your own square root function using the Newton-Raphson method detailed below.

The Newton-Raphson technique allows us to find the root of a function $f(x)$ (i.e. for what value of x does $f(x)$ equal zero). It is based upon the principle of making an approximation for the value of the root (i.e. guess what x is!). We can then use a formula which takes our approximation and returns a better approximation of the root. We can then feed this better approximation back into the formula and get an even better approximation, etc., etc. After only a few cycles our approximations become extremely close to the root that we require.

The formula that we use to produce better approximations is:

$$newx = x - \frac{f(x)}{f'(x)}$$

where $f(x)$ is the function whose root we are looking for (i.e. the value of x which yields zero), x is our last approximation to the root, and $f'(x)$ is the differential of $f(x)$.

To find a square root of a value (y) using this method we need to find the root of this equation:

$$x^2 - y = 0$$

This means that if x is the square root of y then we do get zero. Therefore, we have $f(x) = x^2 - y$ and $f'(x) = 2x$ (differentiate w.r.t. x). Assuming that y is 25, we guess a value for x (say 8) and substitute this into our formula:

$$newx = x - \frac{x^2 - y}{2x}$$

This yields a new approximation of 5.56 and then 5.028, etc. Continuing this process results in values approaching 5, but never actually gets there. We must decide when to stop and this can be done by comparing our new approximation with our last one. If they differ by a small amount (say 0.00001) then we can stop and be left with a fairly accurate result.

3) Using the NR method write a program which reads a real number (y) and an integer number (n) and calculates the nth root of y (e.g. the fourth root of 3.3, the cubed root of -4.5, or the square root of 9). You will find that a variant of the power function written in exercise 1 will be useful in this program.

9 Arrays

9.1 Introduction

We have examined in some detail the manner in which data is stored and represented. However, we have only concentrated on the storage of single items of data, whereas it is very common for a program to handle many hundreds or thousands of items of data. It would clearly be laborious if a programmer had to define thousands of variables individually, so the mechanism for creating arrays of variables in one definition is introduced.

9.2 The concept of arrays

We are familiar with definitions of single variables such as

```
int n;
```

It is possible to define an array of variables in a similar manner. For example

```
int    fred[10];
```

will define ten integer variables, all under the heading *fred* as shown below.

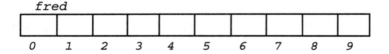

Each of these ten variables is identical to a single variable in the way that it can be manipulated and used, but there is a difference in the manner in which we refer to each of these variables. Unlike single variables we have a number of variables (array elements), all with the same associated identifier *fred*. So that we can distinguish between them, each is also assigned a subscript, which is a number indicating the position of the element in the array, starting from zero. To refer to any array element, we therefore state the associated identifier, followed by a subscript in square brackets. For example, to assign the value 3 to array element 8 of *fred* we would write:

```
fred[8]=3;
```

The array then appears as follows:

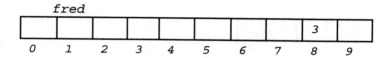

As already stated, array elements can be treated like any single variable and can be used in expressions. For example

```
fred[0]=2;
fred[1]=5;
fred[2]=fred[0]+fred[1];
```

This results in the following:

fred

2	5	7							
0	1	2	3	4	5	6	7	8	9

9.3 Array definitions

As already indicated, an array definition is similar to the definition of a single variable, except that the number of elements required follows the identifier in square brackets. The number of elements is specified using an integer constant, which implies that the number elements required must be known at the time of writing the program. We cannot dynamically create arrays of various sizes as the program runs. Note that the corresponding subscripts resulting from a definition always start from zero. Here are some typical array definitions:

```
#define    array_size 50          Defined constant

int        n[100];                 Integer array 0 to 99
float      list[1000];             Floating point array 0 to 999
char       name[20];               Character array 0 to 19
double     x[array_size];          Double f.p. array 0 to 49
```

It is also possible to define multidimensional arrays as follows:

```
int  table[5][10];
```

This defines an array which can be represented like this:

table

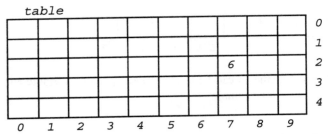

It is possible to define arrays of three or more dimensions simply by adding another number in square brackets to the end of the definition, if required. When referring to a multidimensional array, we must quote the corresponding number of subscripts. For example, the following statement assigns the value 6 to the position shown in the previous diagram.

```
table[2][7]=6;
```

When defining an array we may also need to initialise its elements to some values. This can be done when the array is defined as follows:

```
int primes[8]={1,2,3,5,7,11,13,17};
char triples[4][3]={
                    {'C','A','T'},
                    {'S','A','T'},
                    {'S','E','T'},
                    {'S','E','W'}
                   };
```

These result in the following arrays:

primes   *triples*

1	2	3	5	7	11	13	17
0	1	2	3	4	5	6	7

	0	1	2
0	C	A	T
1	S	A	T
2	S	E	T
3	S	E	W

9.4 Array subscripts

As already seen, array elements are referenced through the use of subscripts. Although this is a fairly straightforward concept, there are a few points worth keeping in mind when using arrays.

Array subscripts are always of integer type and always start at zero. If a non-integer expression is used as a subscript, it will be converted to integer type before use. Therefore, floating point values will be truncated.

Unlike many other high-level languages, in C there is no guarantee that subscripts which are out of range will be detected. This means that if a reference is made to a non-existent element, there will be no error detected. Instead, the program continues running as if the array did extend to the area of memory where the particular element referenced would reside. This could cause corruption of other data or programs, causing unexpected results or program crashes. To illustrate this consider the following section of code:

```
#include <stdio.h>
#define max_primes 10

main()
{
  int n;
  int primes[max_primes]={1,2,3,7,9,11,13,17,19,23};

  for (n=0;n<=max_primes;n++)
  {
    printf(" %i",primes[n]);
  }
}
```

In this program we define and initialise an array of ten values. We then print out these values one at a time, using a *for* loop. Notice that the variable *n* which is the loop counter is used as the array subscript. First time around the loop, *n* will be zero, so we will print *primes[0]*; the next time around, *n* will be 1, and so we will print *primes[1]*, and so on. The output will be

```
1 2 3 7 9 11 13 17 19 23 845
```

We only expect ten values, but instead we get eleven, with the last value being a seemingly random number. This is because the *for* loop executes eleven times (N.B. from 0 to 10 is eleven values). We therefore end up looking at the element *primes[10]* but, remembering that the subscripts always start at zero, the last element defined is *primes[9]*. The last value is the contents of memory where *primes[10]* would reside if the array had been defined to stretch that far. This is clearly not a good situation, and it is something that the programmer must beware of, since there are no run-time checks in C to detect this kind or error. To make the program execute as expected, we need to change the *for* statement to:

```
for(n=0;n<=max_primes-1;n++)
```

or

```
for (n=0;n<max_primes;n++)
```

which makes the loop execute ten times, not eleven.

In this particular example, we can see that it is possible to read values beyond the end of the array, which is unhealthy but at least does not cause damage to other data or program. A worse situation is where the following occurs:

```
scanf ("%i",primes[15]);
```

This will actually write a value to where *primes[15]* would reside if the array was long enough. However, because the array does not extend this far, we will overwrite other variables or program code, causing all sorts of unpredictable effects. Again, it is the responsibility of the programmer to anticipate such problems.

9.5 Self-assessment test − Arrays

What are the values of variables *a*, *b*, *c* and *d* after the following section of program has executed?:

```
int a,b,fred[5]={3,6,1,8,3};
float c,d,bill[3][4]={
                        {4.0,  5.5,  3.0,  0.0},
                        {0.0,  0.1,  2.5,  0.5},
                        {2.5,  3.5,  0.0,  0.8}
                     };

a=fred[2]+fred[0];
b=fred[4]*bill[1][2];
c=bill[0][2]+bill[2][0];
d=fred[2]*bill[0][5];
```

Sketch the array *squares* after the following section of code has executed:

```
int  n,squares[10];

for (n=0;n<10;n++)
{
   squares[n]=n*n;
}
```

Answers: a) 1 + 3 = 4 b) 3*2.5 = 7.5 truncated to 7. c) 3.0 + 2.5 = 5.5 d) Unpredictable, since element *[0][5]* is not defined for this array. However, element *[5]* of the first row would occupy the same memory area as element

[1][1] if all stored in sequence in memory. Therefore result is 1*0.1 = 0.1, but this kind of array access should be avoided.

The array *squares* will have subscripts 0 to 9 and will contain the values 0, 1, 4, 9, 16, 25, 36, 42, 64, 81 (i.e. the squares of the subscripts).

9.6 Passing arrays to functions

We have examined already how we can pass values to a function when it is called using arguments and parameters. We have so far looked only at examples in which the contents of simple variables (as opposed to arrays) are passed to a function. In these circumstances the value of the argument in the function call is copied into a new variable created when the function begins execution. Consequently, the argument and parameter are separate entities residing in different areas in memory.

If the mechanism just described were used for passing an array to a function, it would require a new array to be created as the function begins execution and then all the values from the argument array would need to be copied to the parameter array. Although this is fine in theory, and would be consistent with the way single values are passed, it unfortunately introduces several practical problems, not least of which being the considerable amount of time involved in copying all values of potentially very large arrays. Therefore, a different mechanism is used.

When we pass an array to a function, we are in effect passing just the memory address of the first element of the array in memory. This is a single value which is easily passed without the need for copying the whole contents of the array. Since arrays are stored sequentially in memory, the function can then calculate the position of any element of the array from this starting address and the subscript of the desired element. Hence the argument array and the parameter array may have different associated identifiers, but are physically the same entities occupying the same area of memory.

Notice one problem, namely that by passing just the memory address of the argument array to the function the function will then have no indication of the number of elements in the array. If the function in fact requires this, then a separate value will need to be passed to indicate the size of the array. A simple example of this is a function to read in a sequence of integer values from the keyboard and store them in an array. The function would appear as follows:

```
void read_value(int in_array[], int size)
{
  int n;
  printf("Please enter %i values.",size);
  for (n=0;n<size;n++)
  {
    scanf("%i",&in_array[n]);
```

```
    }
}
```

The first parameter of this function is an array of integers called *in_array* followed by an integer variable called *size*. Notice that the square brackets after *in_array* are empty, indicating that we do not necessarily know how large the array passed from the argument will be. Also, the actual variable created called *in_array* is not itself an array, but a single variable which contains a memory address. Such a variable is called a pointer and the function can use the address that it contains to calculate the address of any element of the array. When referring to *in_array* we treat it as if it were a normal array by specifying a subscript after the identifier. The second parameter *size* will indicate how many values are to be read into the array and so this should be less than, or equal to, the size of the argument array used in the call.

To call this function we may have the following section of code:

```
int   small_array[4], big_array[100];

read_value(small_array,4);
read_value(big_array,50);
```

The first call passes the memory address of *small_array* and indicates that four values are to be read. Inside the function, it is then assumed that *in_array* occupies the same space in memory as *small_array*, so any change made to one will occur in the other. The second call passes the memory address of *big_array*, but the *size* argument is only 50, resulting in only half the array having values read into it.

Note that the type of parameter passing mentioned above applies when a whole array is passed. If a single element of an array is passed, then it is treated as a single variable and so the value of the argument is copied to the parameter. For example, if some function expects a single integer argument, we could call it as follows:

```
some_func(big_array[8]);
```

We are not passing the whole of *big_array* here, but just a single element which is treated in the same manner as any other single integer variable.

9.7 Case study – Statistical analysis

The program that follows reads in ten real numbers from the user and then prints the sum, mean and largest of the values read. The *main* program is simple, as it contains the definition of the array to hold the values read (called *data*), followed by function calls to the appropriate functions to calculate the results.

```
main()
{
  float    data[MAX_VALUES];

  read_value(data,MAX_VALUES);
  printf("\nSum is %f",sum(data,MAX_VALUES));
  printf("\nMean is %f",mean(data,MAX_VALUES));
  printf("\nBiggest value is %f",
     biggest(data,MAX_VALUES));
}
```

The first function called is called *read_value* which reads all the values in the array. It is written as follows:

```
void read_value(float in_array[], int size)
{
  int n;
  for (n=0;n<size;n++)
  {
    scanf("%f",&in_array[n]);
  }
}
```

This function requires two parameters. The first is the array into which the values are read. Remember that with arrays the argument in the function call and the corresponding parameter in the function occupy the same physical area in memory. Therefore, anything placed in the variable *in_array* in this function is also being placed in the variable *data* of the *main* function. On passing an array to a function we can miss out of the parameter definition the size of the array being passed (i.e. nothing in the *[ ]* symbols). This means that this function can work on arrays of all sizes and is more versatile. However, we must now pass a second parameter to indicate the size of the receiving array, which in this case is ten elements. Note that we have used the constant *MAX_VALUES* in preference to writing '10' since the program can then be quickly changed if, for instance, we wanted to deal with 20 numbers. A *for* loop then executes ten times (note that the variable *n* will take values from 0 to 9) and each time we read a value into the next element of *in_array*, which is in effect the same array as *data* from the *main* function.

The next call is to the *sum* function which is written as follows:

```
float sum(float sum_array[],int size)
{
  int n;
  float total;
  total=0;
  for (n=0;n<size;n++)
  {
    total=total+sum_array[n];
```

```
    }
    return total;
}
```

In a similar manner to before, we pass as arguments a reference to the array to be processed and its size. This means that the *sum* function could, if needed, be used on any size of array from zero elements to thousands of elements. Within the *sum* function, the array *data* from the *main* program becomes known as *sum_array* and both occupy the same space in memory. In contrast, the variable *size*, which is a single variable and not an array, is created on calling the function and the value of ten is copied into it. A *for* loop is used to access the array element by element, each time adding the value of each element to a running total in variable *total*. The final value of *total* is then returned.

Notice that the call to the *sum* function is made before the call to *printf* so that the expression to be printed can first be evaluated. We can incorporate the call to *sum* within the call to *printf*, but it does make the program harder to follow. If preferred, we can split this statement up using a *float* variable *x* to become:

```
x = sum (data, MAX_VALUES) ;
printf ("\nSum is %f", x) ;
```

The next function called is *mean*. This is called in a similar way to *sum* but calculates the mean of the array that is passed. The function definition is

```
float mean (float mean_array[], int size)
{
    return sum (mean_array, size) /size;
}
```

Notice that in calculating the mean we need to know the sum of the array, so we call the *sum* function from within the *mean* function. The result of this we divide by the number of elements in the array given by the variable *size*. It could be considered slightly inefficient in that we have called *sum* twice at this point, whereas we could have preserved the value from the previous call, but this can be tolerated here.

The final function returns the largest value in the array. This is done by assuming that the first element of the array contains the biggest value and this value is stored in the variable *biggest_yet*. The program then compares the value of *biggest_yet* with each of the other elements of the array. Each time a value larger than *biggest_yet* is encountered, we update *biggest_yet* to this value. At the end of the *for* loop we will have been right through the array, so *biggest_yet* will contain the largest value in the array.

The complete program is as follows:

```
/* Program to read a sequence of real numbers and */
/* print the sum, mean and largest                 */
#include <stdio.h>
#define MAX_VALUES 10 /*Number of values processed*/

/* Function prototypes */
void read_value(float in_array[], int size);
float sum(float sum_array[],int size);
float mean(float mean_array[], int size);
float biggest(float big_array[], int size);

/***********************************************/
main()
{
  float    data[MAX_VALUES];

  read_value(data,MAX_VALUES);
  printf("\nSum is %f",sum(data,MAX_VALUES));
  printf("\nMean is %f",mean(data,MAX_VALUES));
  printf("\nBiggest value is %f",
      biggest(data,MAX_VALUES));
}

/***********************************************/
/* Reads in 'size' values to array 'in_array'  */

void read_value(float in_array[], int size)
{
  int n;

  printf("Please enter %i values:",size);
  for (n=0;n<size;n++)
  {
    scanf("%f",&in_array[n]);
  }
}

/***********************************************/
/*Function which calculates sum  of array of size */
/* 'sum_array' of size 'size'.  Returns result    */

float sum(float sum_array[],int size)
{
  int n;
  float total;

  total=0;
  for (n=0;n<size;n++)
  {
    total=total+sum_array[n];
  }
  return total;
```

```
}
/****************************************************/
/* Function which returns mean of the values of    */
/* array 'mean_array' of size 'size'               */

float mean(float mean_array[], int size)
{
  return sum(mean_array,size)/size;
}

/***********************************************/
/* Function which returns the largest value    */
/* in the array 'big_array' of size 'size'     */

float biggest(float big_array[], int size)
{
  float biggest_yet;
  int n;

  biggest_yet=big_array[0];
  for (n=1;n<size;n++)
  {
    if (big_array[n]>biggest_yet)
    {
      biggest_yet=big_array[n];
    }
  }
  return biggest_yet;
}
```

An example of a typical session using this function is as follows:

```
Please enter 10 values: 1.0 3.0 5.0 7.0 9.0 8.0 6.0 4.0 2.0 0.0
Sum is 45.000000
Mean is 4.500000
Biggest value is 9.000000
```

9.8 Algorithm design

We have reached a stage where the types of program that we are studying are becoming fairly complex. Consequently, we will pause for a while from studying more of the C language and look at how we go about designing programs to perform complex tasks.

Firstly, it is important to be able to define exactly what the program or function to be written will perform. We will concentrate on tasks such as searching an array for a particular value, or sorting a list of values into order. In order to design our program we must produce an algorithm, which is a term applied to a set of instructions which, when executed, will perform some task. The C language is a method of describing an algorithm to a computer such that it can then perform the actual task. Thus, in initially designing an algorithm it might be easier to use something more friendly than C, such as natural English, but the problem is that English lacks any formal structure. Instead, a combination of programming language and English is used; this is referred to as pseudocode, which we will now examine.

Pseudocode is a set of English statements describing a task, but using C type structures such as *if* statements, loops and variables. As an example, consider a problem where we need to search an array of integers to see if it contains the value 5. This can be expressed in pseudocode as follows (with C statements in bold):

```
set flag to 0
for each element of array
{
  if array element equals 5 set flag to 1
}
if flag equals 1 print 'Array contains the value 5'
       else     print 'Array does not contain a 5'
```

This is easy to follow and verify by the programmer, but we must now turn it into a C program. This means refining each part of the pseudocode in comfortable steps until it looks like complete C. A refined version of this section of code could become:

```
flag=0
for (n equals each array subscript)
{
  if array[n]==5 then flag=1
}
if (flag==1)then printf("Array contains a 5")
          else printf("Array does not contain a 5")
```

The next refinement then results in the final C program. We assume that the name of the array is *value_list* from here on and is of length given by a constant called *list_length*. We also assume that *flag* and *n* are defined as integer variables:

```
flag=0;
for (n=0;n<list_length;n++)
{
  if (value_list[n]==5) flag=1;
}
if (flag==1) printf("Array contains a 5");
     else    printf("Array does not contain a 5");
```

This method of stepwise refinement can be very useful in designing small programs and the reader is encouraged to try using it in future exercises. We will use it in the next section, where we examine an important aspect of array processing, namely sorting.

9.9 Sorting arrays

A common task when using arrays is to have to sort the array into ascending or descending order. There are many different ways of achieving this, but we will concentrate on a simple algorithm called bubble sorting. Consider the array of ten integers below, called value_list:

```
value_list
0    12
1    34
2    22
3    15
4    40
5    26
6    31
7    22
8    14
9    12
```

To sort this into ascending order using a bubble sort algorithm, we move down the array comparing each element with its next neighbour. If the two elements are in ascending order then they are not moved, but if they are in descending order then they are swapped around. In this example, we first compare elements 0 and 1 which are in ascending order, so we move on to compare elements 1 and 2. These are in descending order (i.e. $34 > 22$), so they are swapped. We then compare elements 2 and 3 and, remembering that element 2 is now equal to 32, we find that these are in descending order, so they are swapped. We continue until we have compared elements 8 and 9 and then the array will appear as follows:

```
value_list
0    12
1    22
2    15
3    34
4    26
5    31
6    22
7    14
8    12
9    40
```

At the end of the cycle, we find that the largest value (40) will end up at the bottom of the array. This can be thought of as the heaviest sinking to the bottom while all the lighter values 'bubble' up around it, hence the name of the algorithm. However, the array is not completely sorted, although at least the bottom value is in its correct position. If we repeat the process we will eventually find that the array will be left in ascending order, so that we obtain:

```
value_list
0  | 12 |
1  | 12 |
2  | 14 |
3  | 15 |
4  | 22 |
5  | 22 |
6  | 26 |
7  | 31 |
8  | 34 |
9  | 40 |
```

To ensuree that the array is sorted, we may need to make nine passes through the array. The algorithm to perform this task can be described in pseudocode as:

```
for a number of times equal to the array length-1
{
  for each element down the array except the last
  {
    compare the value of the element with the next one
    below in the array and if the next element is
    smaller then swap the values of these two elements
  }
```

In the next refinement we will assume that the array is called *value_list* and is of length *list_length* and that we have an integer variable called *n*, which controls a *for* loop, and *temp*, which is used to hold a value while swapping the values of two array elements.

```
for (list_length-1 iterations)
{
  for (n equals 0 to list_len-2)
  {
    if (value_list[n]>value_list[n+1])
    {
      temp=value_list[n]
      value_list[n]=value_list[n+1]
      value_list[n+1]=temp
    }
  }
}
```

The final refinement here results in a complete function called *sort* which will sort any integer array passed to it of a size given by the parameter *size*.

```
void sort(int value_list[], int size)
{
  int n,m,temp;

  for (m=1;m<size;m++)
  {
    for (n=0;n<=size-2;n++)
    {
     if (value_list[n]>value_list[n+1]
     {
        temp=value_list[n];
        value_list[n]=value_list[n+1];
        value_list[n+1]=temp;
     }
    }
  }
}
```

Notice that this algorithm can be made more efficient in two ways. It may be that the array is almost, or even completely, in order from the start, and so we will end up going through the whole process without moving anything. Therefore, if we test after each pass if nothing has moved, then the array is ordered and so the process can terminate early. Also, after the first pass the largest value will be in its correct position, so we can ignore it on the next pass. After this next pass the second heaviest value will lie second from the bottom and so on. Therefore, on each pass we can reduce the distance that we need to travel down the array by one, since it is guaranteed that the tail end is already in order.

For small tasks the function shown will be sufficient, but for sorting large arrays it is found that the execution time increases with the square on the number of array elements and so this algorithm can become very inefficient.

9.10 Summary

- Arrays allow a large number of identical variables to be created easily with a single definition.

- Array elements are referenced by the array identifier followed by the elements subscript.

- Array subscripts always start from zero. There is no guarantee of run-time range checking of subscripts.

- An array type parameter of a function occupies the same memory area as the array used as the argument in the call. This is in contrast to single variables, where the parameter and argument are separate entities and the value of the argument is copied to the parameter on calling the function.

- Arrays can be multidimensional and so may require more than one subscript.

9.11 Exercises

1) Write a program to read in a set of ten real numbers and then normalise them. That is to say the numbers in the array should all be scaled by the same factor such that they sum to 1. Work this through on paper first, so that you understand the problem. The resulting values in the array should then be printed.

2) The diagram below represents a room containing obstacles which is to be navigated by a small robot. The robot starts travelling in a random direction and on collision with an obstacle or wall the robot should change its course to a new random direction. Write a program to simulate the robot and assess its performance when it is only allowed to move from one square to the next in

   a) north, south, east or west directions
   b) north, south, east, west and the four diagonal directions.

   The room can be represented by a two-dimensional integer array where a 1 entry represents an obstacle and 0 represents open space. The aim is that the robot should reach point B from point A.

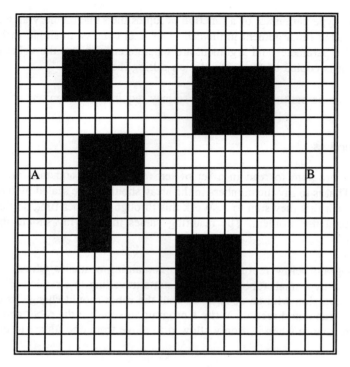

To produce random values which can be used to choose directions use the *rand* function, which returns a random integer number each time it is called between 0 and the largest positive value that an *int* can represent (usually 32768). After each successful move, the new coordinates of the robot should be printed and, on arrival at the destination, the total number of moves made should be printed.

3) Write a program to read in 20 real numbers and then print their mean, median and mode. In order to find the median and mode, it is necessary to sort the array into order.

10 Strings

10.1 Introduction

We have examined arrays and how they can be used to hold a sequence of values accessed using subscripts. There is a special mode of using arrays when they are composed of *char* type variables which allows us to access and use the array in a different manner. Such arrays can be used to hold a string of characters which can be manipulated as a whole entity, making the processing of text and words much simpler.

10.2   String variables

In order to hold a string of characters we must define an array such as:

```
char  surname[10];
```

This sets up ten character variables in sequence, which in this case we can now use to hold surnames up to ten letters long. We can initialise the value of the string when we define it such as:

```
char firstname[7]="Dominic";
char surname[7]="Bury";
```

The first definition here results in an array which appears as follows:

firstname

D	o	m	i	n	i	c
0	1	2	3	4	5	6

In this case the array is exactly long enough to hold the string assigned to it. However, the next definition creates an array that is seven elements long, but contains a string that is only four letters long. In this case an extra character is assigned to the fifth character position to indicate that the string terminates at this point. The special character used is a non-printable character, but is represented using the escape sequence \0 and is called the string termination character. The resulting array therefore appears as follows:

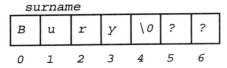

Notice that the two empty elements at the end of the array are not assigned any values and so their contents is unknown. The string terminator character is detected by string processing functions which recognise the meaning of this character.

It is possible to define an array just large enough to hold the string that it is initialised with. For example:

```
char firstname[]="Fred";
```

results in the following array being created:

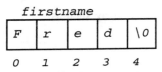

Notice that this results in an array which has a terminating character placed on the end. It is best to ensure that all strings have a terminating character so that they can be properly processed by those functions that use this character as the only means of determining where the string ends.

10.3   Input and output of strings

To print a string we use *printf*. We can simply quote a string constant, as we have done often, such as:

```
printf("Hello");
```

To print the contents of a string variable, we would use the *%s* format code, just as we use *%i* for integers or *%f* for floats. For example:

```
char greeting[]="Hi there!";
printf("%s",greeting);
```

This results in the message 'Hi there!' appearing. To read a string, we use the *%s* format code with *scanf*. For example:

```
char surname[10];
scanf("%s",surname);
```

There are two important things to note here. First is that there is no & symbol used in *scanf* before the name of the receiving variable. This is peculiar only to strings. Also, notice that the receiving string is only ten elements long. Therefore, if the user enters 'Jones', when this is read into the array there is room to add on a terminating character after the 's'. However, if the user enters 'Smythe-Pigot' which is considerably longer than ten letters, then *scanf* will read all of this in and write it into and over the end of the array. This may well mean that other data or program code in memory may be overwritten, causing very odd effects. It is therefore up to the programmer to ensure that the receiving arrays are large enough for the expected input. It is usually good policy to make the arrays very much bigger than the expected input. Also, we can limit the maximum size of the resulting string by using a format code such as *%12s*, meaning that at most twelve characters are read by *scanf*.

When reading input, *scanf* will assume that a string starts at the first non-space character encountered and ends at the next space or carriage return. Therefore, the space and carriage return characters are called delimiters, as they indicate the limits of the string. Consequently, if we have the following statement:

```
scanf("%s",surname);
```

this will successfully read a line typed by the user such as 'Bloggs'. However, if the user types 'Fred Bloggs' then *scanf* will only read up to the space after 'Fred' and leaves 'Bloggs' in the keyboard buffer. It is possible to change the delimiters used by *scanf* but the need for this by novices is not anticipated.

When reading strings, it is always a good idea to ensure that the keyboard buffer is empty, by preceding the *scanf* statement with *fflush*, as shown:

```
char surname[50], Title[10];

printf("Please enter your surname with no spaces");
fflush(stdin);   /* Clear keyboard buffer */
scanf("%49s",surname);
printf("Please enter your title (Mr,Mrs etc)");
fflush(stdin);
scanf("%s",title);
printf("Hello %s %s",title,surname);
```

This section of code prompts the user for their title and surname and then prints a message such as:

```
Hello Mrs Smith
```

Notice that we can define an empty string, such as:

```
char surname[50]="";
```

This results in a space in memory being created fifty bytes long and the first element is a termination character.

10.4   String assignment

In contrast to other simple variables, we cannot assign strings using an assignment statement such as:

```
surname="Jones";
```

Although this is a reasonable operation in principle, the compiler does not allow it in the interests of keeping the compiler simple. Instead, we must use a standard library function for copying strings to assign a value. There is a whole set of library functions for dealing with strings, some of which we will see later. Note that when using string library functions we must include the *string.h* header file. The string copy function has the following form:

```
strcpy(destination_string,source_string);
```

This copies the contents of the source string up to and including the termination character to the destination string. It is assumed that the destination string is defined to be long enough to hold the string copied to it. If it is not, other data could be overwritten, so the programmer must be cautious.

It is possible to use an assignment statement to directly manipulate a single character by treating the string as an array. For example:

```
surname[2]='Z';
```

This sets the third element of the surname string to 'Z'. Notice that single quotes are used when dealing with single character variables and double quotes for strings (even if they are one character long). Here is a section of code demonstrating these operations:

```
/* String assignment demo */

#include <string.h>    /* Required for strcpy */
#include <ctype.h>   /* Required for toupper */

main()
{
  char surname[10], new_surname[10], firstletter;

  strcpy(surname,"evans");
  strcpy(new_surname,surname);
```

```
firstletter=new_surname[0];
firstletter=toupper(firstletter);
new_surname[0]=firstletter;
printf("%s %s",surname,new_surname);
}
```

In this program, we initially use the *strcpy* function to set the string called *surname* to contain 'evans', which is then also copied to the string called *new_surname*. We then assign the first character of *new_surname* to the character variable *firstletter*. This is then converted to upper case, using the function *toupper* which converts its argument to upper case if it is a lower case letter, or otherwise returns the argument untouched. Therefore, *firstletter* will now become 'E'. This is then assigned to the first element of *new_surname* so that the final message printed will be:

```
evans Evans
```

10.5   String comparison

We cannot use the usual forms of conditional expressions that we are familiar with when dealing with single variables for testing the values of strings. For example, the following is not allowed, where *surname* is a string type variable:

```
if (surname=="Smith") ......
```

To compare two strings, we must use a standard library function called *strcmp* which accepts two strings as arguments and returns an integer value which is zero if the two strings are identical, a negative value if the first string is less than the second string (alphabetically or according to the ASCII sequence), or a positive number if the first string is greater than the second. Its general form is:

```
strcmp(string1,string2)
```

For example, to test if someone's surname is 'Jones' we could write:

```
char surname[20]="";

printf("Please enter your surname ");
fflush(stdin);
scanf("%s",surname);
if ( strcmp(surname,"Jones")==0 )
    printf("I know you!");
else
    printf("Never heard of you!");
```

Here the user's reply is stored in *surname* and then the *strcmp* function is called (from within a conditional expression) to compare *surname* with the string constant 'Jones'. The return value is then tested to see if it is zero, indicating that the strings match. The *if* statement then acts accordingly. Notice that if the user typed 'Evans' then *strcmp* would return a negative value, since this is alphabetically lower than 'Jones'. If the user typed 'jones' then a positive value would be returned because 'j' and 'J' are seen as different and, since 'j' occurs further down the ASCII code sequence, the first string is deemed to be greater than 'Jones'.

10.6   Case conversion

Since the string comparison function is case sensitive, it is often useful to have a function available to convert a string to all upper or lower case letters before performing a comparison. There is no standard function available for this, but a non-standard one may be supplied with certain compilers. If none is available then the following function can be used:

```
void str_upper(char str[])
{
  int n;

  n=0;
  while (str[n] !='\0')
  {
    str[n]=toupper(str[n]);
    n++;
  }
}
```

This function accepts one argument which becomes the parameter *str* in this function. Remember that when arrays are passed as arguments the argument and parameter arrays are the same (i.e. they occupy the same area of memory). Hence any changes made to *str* in this function are also made to the array used as an argument in the call. The principle is to scan the string element by element converting each to upper case until a termination character is encountered. The variable *n* is used as a subscript for the array and is incremented after each character is processed. The library function *toupper* is used to convert each character to upper case if required. Note that there is also a *tolower* function available and that both these functions require the header file *ctype.h* to be included (N.B. *toupper* and *tolower* are often implemented as macros; these are different to functions but in this case can be used in a similar manner). This function may be called as follows using a string called *case_string* which contains 'helLO 123$':

```
str_upper(case_string);
```

After this call *case_string* will contain 'HELLO 123$'. Note that the argument must contain a terminator character, otherwise the function will continue converting whatever is in memory after the string until it eventually finds a termination character, possibly causing devastation. This is general for most string functions.

10.7   String library functions

There are a number of standard library functions defined for processing strings, although there may be other non-standard functions supplied with certain compilers. They all require the file *string.h* to be included and assume that strings are terminated with the terminator character '\0'. It is the programmer's responsibility to ensure that the strings are large enough to hold anything placed in them by these functions. Some of these functions are briefly described below:

`strcmp(string1,string2)`	Compares strings as previously described.
`strcat(string1,string2)`	Copies (concatenates) *string2* on to the end of *string1*.
`strlen(string)`	Returns an integer which is the length of the string excluding the termination character.
`strcpy(string1,string2)`	Copies *string2* to *string1*.

10.8   String value conversions

It is common to need to convert, say the value of an integer variable to its corresponding string, or to convert a string of numerals to an integer type value. There are functions available specifically to do this but, for consistency, we will stick to functions which are similar to *printf* and *scanf* with which we are familiar. Consider a situation we are familiar with, which is to print the value of an integer:

```
n=789;
printf("%i",n);
```

The *printf* function will convert the binary value of variable *n* to a three-character string '789'. These characters are then sent to the display hardware so that they appear on the monitor. However, if we do not want the resulting string to be sent to the monitor, but want it to be stored in a string variable where we may manipulate it further, we can use a function called *sprintf*. This works exactly the same as *printf*, except that instead of the resulting string appearing on the monitor, it is saved in a string given as the first argument. The general form of the call is:

```
sprintf(receiving_str., format_str., sub._values);
```

For example, we may have the following section of code:

```
char   numerals[10];
int n;

n=789;
sprintf(numerals,"%i",n);
```

The result is exactly the same as the previous *printf* example, but the resulting string '789' is placed in *numerals* (with a termination character) and not on the monitor. The *sprintf* function can do anything that *printf* can do, so we can convert floating point values, using *%f* or *%g*, and also impose formatting of the resulting strings (e.g. use the format code *%6.3f*).

The reverse procedure, where a string of numeral characters is converted to an *int* or *float* value, is possible using a function similar to *scanf*. The *scanf* function reads a string from the keyboard and converts it to the appropriate representation for the receiving variable. For example, to read an integer, we write:

```
scanf("%i",&n);
```

The *sscanf* function is almost identical, but instead of processing a string of characters entered from the keyboard, it processes a string given as an additional argument. The general form of a call is:

```
sscanf(input_str., format_str.,&receiving_variable);
```

An example of its usage is shown below:

```
char numerals="123";
int n;

sscanf(numerals,"%i",&n);
```

At the end of this the value of *n* will be 123. As with *scanf*, if the input cannot be converted (e.g. if it contains letters) then the conversion is aborted. The function returns an integer value (as does *scanf*), indicating how many values were successfully converted. We can convert strings to other types using the appropriate format codes.

When using *sscanf* or *sprintf*, the *stdio.h* header file is required. There are other functions which perform similar tasks, such as *atof*, *atoi*, and *atol*, which the reader may like to investigate.

10.9   Self-assessment test − Strings

What strings (including termination characters) or integer values, result from the following definitions and statements (assume where required the existence of a twenty-element string called *str2* containing the word 'Pacific')?:

```
a) char str[10]="Fred";      b) char str[]="Harry";
c) char str[5]="James";      d) str="Hello";
e) strcpy(str,str2);          f) strlen(str2)
g) strcat(str2," Ocean");    h) strcmp("Atlantic",str2);
i) sprintf(str,"%4i",23);    j)sprintf(str,"%10.2e",0.666);
```

Answers: a) 'Fred\0'+5 empty elements. b) 'Harry\0'. c) 'James' Note no terminator! d) Illegal. Cannot assign strings like this. e) *str* and *str2* both contain 'Pacific\0'. f) Returns 7. g) *str2* becomes 'Pacific Ocean\0'. h) Returns negative value. i) *str* becomes '23'. Note two leading spaces. j) *str* becomes ' 6.67e-001\0'. One leading space.

10.10   Case study − Resistor calculator

The following example is a program to read in the colours of the bands of a three-banded resistor and print the corresponding resistance in ohms. The first band read is the first digit, the second band is the second digit and the third band is the exponent (i.e. multiply by a power of ten). The main program in outline is as follows:

```
int band1,band2,band3,n;
long int resistance;

band1=readband();
band2=readband();
band3=readband();

resistance=10*band1+band2;

for (n=0;n<band3;n++)
{
  resistance=resistance*10;
}
```

```
printf("\nResistance is %li Ohms.",resistance);
```

We have three integer variables, each of which will hold the value of a colour band from 0 to 9. Each is set by a function called *readband*, which reads a colour from the user and returns the appropriate integer value. From these three values we can then calculate the final resistance. The loop multiplies the resistance by ten according the value of *band3* which adds the correct number of zeros. Notice that a *long int* is used for the final result, since it can be a large value. The readband function is defined as follows:

```
int readband(void)
{
  char colour[10];

  do
  {
    fflush(stdin);
    scanf("%9s",colour);
    str_upper(colour);

    if ( strcmp(colour,"BLACK"  )==0) return 0;
    if ( strcmp(colour,"BROWN"  )==0) return 1;
    if ( strcmp(colour,"RED"    )==0) return 2;
       .                   .
       .                   .
    if ( strcmp(colour,"WHITE"  )==0) return 9;

    /*If this point reached no match made. Error!*/
    printf("Colour not recognised. Try again. ");
  }
  while (1);  /* Always loops back */
}
```

A string is read using *scanf* and is then converted to upper case, using a function similar to that described in section 10.6. This string is then compared to a sequence of colour names using *strcmp*. If a match is found, the appropriate value is returned and the function ends. If no match is found, we will reach the end of the *do-while* loop. A message is printed and then the loop reiterates to allow the user to retype the input. The complete program is as follows:

```
/* Program to read the three bands of a resistor */
/* and print the corresponding resistance in ohms */

#include <stdio.h>
#include <string.h>
#include <ctype.h>

/* Function prototypes */
void str_upper(char str[]);
```

```
int readband(void);

/* Main program                                       */

main()
{
  int band1,band2,band3,n;
  long int resistance;

  /* Read band values */
  printf("Enter three bands of resistor\n");
  printf("Band 1:-");
  band1=readband();
  printf("Band 2:-");
  band2=readband();
  printf("Band 3:-");
  band3=readband();

  /* Calculate digits */
  resistance=10*band1+band2;

  /* Loop for the number of times given by band 3 */
  /* Multiply up by 10 each time */
  for (n=0;n<band3;n++)
  {
    resistance=resistance*10;
  }
  printf("\nResistance is %li Ohms.",resistance);
}

/**************************************************/
/* Reads colour and returns corresponding         */
/* integer value. Checks for errors.              */

int readband(void)
{
  char colour[10];

  do
  {
    /* Read string and convert to upper case */
    fflush(stdin);
    scanf("%9s",colour);
    str_upper(colour);

    /*Test string and return appropriate value*/
    if ( strcmp(colour,"BLACK"  )==0) return 0;
    if ( strcmp(colour,"BROWN"  )==0) return 1;
    if ( strcmp(colour,"RED"    )==0) return 2;
    if ( strcmp(colour,"ORANGE" )==0) return 3;
    if ( strcmp(colour,"YELLOW" )==0) return 4;
    if ( strcmp(colour,"GREEN"  )==0) return 5;
```

```
    if ( strcmp(colour,"BLUE"   )==0) return 6;
    if ( strcmp(colour,"VIOLET" )==0) return 7;
    if ( strcmp(colour,"GREY"   )==0) return 8;
    if ( strcmp(colour,"WHITE"  )==0) return 9;

    /*If this point reached no match made. Error!*/
    printf("\n\aColour not recognised.Try again.");
  }
  while (1);   /* always loops back */
}
/*********************************************/
/* Converts string to upper case            */

void str_upper(char str[])
{
  int n;

  n=0;
  while (str[n]!='\0')
  {
    str[n]=toupper(str[n]);
    n++;
  }
}
```

10.11 Summary

- Strings are arrays of characters. Unlike other arrays, which can only be manipulated as single elements, strings can also can be manipulated as a single entity.

- Strings use a special terminator character to mark their end in the array. The escape sequence for the terminator character is '\0'. This character must be present when using string library functions.

- No limit checking is performed when using strings. Therefore, it is the programmer's responsibility to ensure that no string is larger than the array defined to hold it and that all strings have termination characters.

- Strings cannot be assigned or tested in the same way as simple variables. Instead, standard library functions are provided to perform these tasks.

- Strings of numerals can be converted to any number representation using *sscanf*. A value held in any number representation can be converted to a numerical string, using *sprintf*.

10.12 Exercises

1) Write a program to read in a single word and print its length, the word in upper case and the entire word backwards.

2) Write a program which reads a word and tests if it is a palindrome (i.e. the same if spelt backwards, e.g. 'madam').

11 File Input and Output

11.1 Introduction

We have already seen how we can make programs interact with the outside world using input and output functions associated with the keyboard and monitor. However, it is common for programs to read and write information to or from files on disk, as well as interacting with the user. The mechanism for performing file operations is very similar to those for input and output which we have already seen. We will cover here the basics which are sufficient for the vast majority of tasks.

11.2 File structure

A file is usually an area or sequence of linked areas on a magnetic disk which often contains text (i.e. strings of bytes containing ASCII codes) or binary values (e.g. strings of bits representing integer numbers or floating point numbers). We will concentrate on text files, as these will be adequate for our requirements. The file system structure is managed by the operating system and so our C programs do not manipulate the disk directly, but instead make requests to the operating system which then performs the required task and passes back any information to our program. This approach makes our programs simple, enables programs to function with different filing systems, and also protects the filing system if our program runs haywire.

A text file can be represented as follows. A file of names (one on each line) may appear as follows:

authors.txt

```
Thomas Hardy\n
Oscar Wilde\n
        .

        .

Antony Trollope\n
George Orwell[EOF]
```

Notice that each line is terminated with a newline character (the escape sequence for this is \n) and that the end of the file is marked in some way (denoted above as *[EOF]* for 'End of File'). Each file on the system also has a name and a path which denotes in which directory from the root of the disk it is found. In the above example the filename is *authors.txt*.

144

11.3   Opening and closing files

Before we can read or write to a file we must identify which file of the hundreds on the system we wish to use and whether it will be used for reading or writing (i.e. input or output). This process is called opening a file. To open a file we use the library function *fopen* which expects two arguments that are both strings. The first string is the file name (plus the path if required) and the second denotes whether the file is opened for reading or writing. For example:

```
fopen ("/people/authors.txt","r");
```

opens the file called *authors.txt* in the directory *people* for reading. There are three possibilities for the second argument:

"r"   Open file for reading.

"w"   Open file for writing. If the file already exists, its original contents is erased. If the file does not exist, then it is created.

"a"   Open file for writing. Anything written to file is appended to the end of the existing file. If the file does not exist, then it is created.

When a file is opened, a block of data is created containing information about the file, including its position, mode (read or write), size, etc. All the input and output routines access the file through this block of data and so we need to make a note of its position in memory. We can do this because the *fopen* function returns a value which is the memory address of the start of the file data block. We need to save this value so that it can be passed to the various input and output functions, as we will see later. The value returned by *fopen* is of a type new to us, called *FILE* (it is an example of a pointer which is covered later), and so we need a variable defined of this type to hold the value for future reference. Notice a peculiarity here that when defining a variable of type *FILE* its name is prefixed with a '*' in the definition. The reason for this is covered in the chapter on pointers. Therefore, to open a file properly, we need something such as:

```
FILE *myfile;    /* Define file pointer variable */

myfile=fopen ("/people/authors.txt","a");
```

If successful, then all future input and output functions can refer to the file */people/authors.txt* through the variable *myfile* as will be seen later. It is often the case that *fopen* is not successful. For example, if we try to open a file from which to read which does not exist, then *fopen* will fail. Also, opening a file for writing on a write-protected disk will fail. We can detect this because *fopen* will return a special value denoted by the constant *NULL*. This is demonstrated in a complete section of code below in which the file *data.dat* is opened for reading.

```
#include <stdio.h>   /*required for file functions*/
#include <stdlib.h> /* required for exit function */

main ()
{
  FILE *infile;

  infile=fopen("data.dat","r");
  if (infile==NULL)
  {
    printf("Error opening file");
    exit(0);   /* terminates program */
  }
  .
  .
  (rest of program)
  .
}
```

This section of program attempts to open the file and, if successful, returns the memory address of the file information block to the variable *infile,* which is used for future references to the file. If *fopen* is unsuccessful, it returns a value of *NULL*. This triggers the *if* statement, which prints a message and the then calls a function called *exit*. This function causes the program to terminate at this point since we cannot continue because the file is not open. Note that when using the standard library function *exit* we must include the header file $<stdlib.h>$ and the function must have an integer argument (its value is not important, zero used here).

When a file is finished with, we can instruct the operating system to tidy up the end of the file in a process called closing the file. To close a file we simply call the function *fclose* with the file pointer variable as an argument. For example, at the end of the program in the previous example, we might have:

```
fclose(infile);
```

Files are usually closed automatically when a program terminates, but it is generally good practice to close them specifically using *fclose*.

A small point worth noting concerns the quoting of pathnames when using the MS-DOS operating system on IBM-PC type machines. This file system uses the backslash (\) as a delimiter which, if quoted in a string, is interpreted as the start of an escape code. In this case we must use the escape sequence for a backslash which is '\\'.

11.4 Writing to files

Once a file has been opened for writing, then to actually write the information to it is simple. The process uses a standard library function called *fprintf* which is almost identical to *printf* with which we are familiar. The only difference is that *fprintf* has an extra argument which is the file pointer for the file to which data is written. A generalised call is as follows:

```
fprintf(file_pointer, format_string, values);
```

For example, to write the string 'Hello' to a file referenced by the file pointer variable *greetfile*, we would write:

```
fprintf(greetfile, "Hello");
```

We can write out complex formatted strings just as we have done with *printf*. Here is an example which writes all the powers of 2 to a file, each separated with a newline:

```
/* Writes all the powers of two form 0 to 10 */
/* to a file called power.two                 */
#include     <stdio.h>
#include     <stdlib.h>

main()
{
  FILE      *outfile;
  int       n, power;

  /* Open file. Terminate if unsuccessful */
  outfile=fopen("power.two","w");
  if (outfile==NULL)
  {
    printf("Cannot open file");
    exit(0);
  }

  /* Loop ten times. Each time double power and */
  /* write it to file                           */
  power=1;
  for (n=0;n<=10;n++)
  {
    fprintf(outfile,"%i \n",power);
    power=power*2;
  }
  fclose(outfile);
}
```

When printed the resulting file called *power.two* appears as follows:

```
1
2
4
8
16
32
64
128
256
512
1024
```

11.5   Reading from files

To read data from a file we use a function called *fscanf*, which is almost identical in operation to *scanf*, but requires an extra argument to identify the opened file from which to read data. The general form of a call to *fscanf* is as follows:

```
fscanf(file_pointer,format_str,receiving_variables);
```

Here is an example which assumes the existence of a file containing ten integer numbers called *values.dat*. This program opens this file for reading, then reads each number into the variable *sum* and adds it to a running total in variable *total*. This requires a loop which runs ten times to read all ten numbers. Finally, the average of the values in the file is printed.

```
int n,sum,total,status;
FILE *datafile;

datafile=fopen("values.dat","r");
if (datafile==NULL)
{
  printf("Error opening file");
  exit(0);
}

/* File open. Read ten numbers and sum */
total=0;
for (n=1;n<=10;n++)
{
  fscanf(datafile,"%i",&sum);
  total=total+sum;
}

/* print result */
printf("Average of values in file= %i",total/10) ;
```

Notice an important concept here. We assume that when we open a file the first value read is taken from the beginning of the file. After this value is read, the next value read is the second one in the file, and so on. Each file therefore has an associated position marker, which indicates where the next read operation will take its data from in the file. This indicator is advanced as required after each read operation is performed.

A more general case of the previous example is where it is not known how many values the file contains (we assumed that it was ten values). A more versatile program will read all the values in the file, no matter how many there are and then print their average. This requires us to be able to detect when the file position indicator has hit the end of the file, so that we know when to stop reading values. This is done using the return value from *fscanf*, as now described.

We have already seen that *scanf* returns an integer value indicating how many values it has read and successfully converted to the required representation. This value can be used to detect a case when *scanf* is asked to read an integer, but is presented with something like '*6y%$', rather than something like '67'. In addition to this *fscanf*, returns a specific value if it fails in a conversion, due to an attempt to read past the end of the file. It usually returns -1, but this value may change between different implementations. To avoid problems, the value returned is associated with the identifier *EOF*, using a *#define* directive in the header file *stdio.h* which we must include. Therefore, if *fscanf* returns a value equal to *EOF*, then the program has tried to read past the end of the file. Here is a program similar to the previous example, but which does not assume anything about the length of the file:

```
int count,sum,total,status;
FILE *datafile;

datafile=fopen("values.dat","r");
if (datafile==NULL)
{
  printf("Error opening file");
  exit(0);
}

/* File open. Read values and sum */
total=0;     /* Running total */
count=0;     /* Counts values read */
do
{
  status=fscanf(datafile,"%i",&sum);

  /* If valid value read then add to total */
  if (status==1)
```

```
{
    total=total+sum;
    count=count+1;
}

/* If invalid value read print message and end */
if (status==0)
{
    printf("Error reading value %i",count+1);
    exit(0);
}
}
while (status!=EOF);

/* Reached end of file. Print result */
printf("Average of values is %i",total/count);
```

Notice that if the file contains text which does not represent a valid integer, this will be detected by this program. The result is an error message and then the program will terminate. It is possible to have the program continue after the error in the file to read subsequent values and produce a result. This is a little bit fiddly, but not too difficult. However, for our purposes the approach that the program terminates with an error message will suffice for now. An example of the sort of error that we may encounter is when reading a file of data, such as:

```
23

45

56

abc

78

50

[EOF]
```

This will cause the program to terminate with the error message

```
Error reading value 4
```

11.6   Opening user-specified files

In all the examples so far, the filenames used have been set by the programmer within the program. A more flexible approach is to allow the user to specify the filenames to be used when the program is running. Consider the previous example, where the program always reads its data from the file *values.dat*, which makes the program very limited. A more useful program would be one which asks the user from which file to read the data; this allows the program to process any file of appropriate data. This is achieved by using a string variable containing the filename in our call to *fopen*, rather than a string constant as we have done previously. This is illustrated below for opening a file for reading:

```
char fname[50];
FILE *datafile;

/* Loop until file successfully opened */
do
{
  printf("Enter filename or hit enter to quit");
  fflush(stdin);
  scanf("%49s",fname);

  /* File name read. Now try to open file */
  datafile=fopen(fname,"r");
  if (datafile==NULL)
  {
    printf("Cannot find or open file");
  }
}
while (datafile==NULL);
```

This section of code prompts the user for a filename. It then reads the response into the string variable *fname*. This string is then used by *fopen* and if the file is successfully opened then the loop will terminate. If the file is not opened (e.g. it does not exist), then the loop re-executes, prompting the user again for a new filename. There is one small potential problem with this section of code in that the user must enter a valid filename; there is no other escape from this loop should the user wish to give up and terminate the program. There are, however, ways to fix this if required.

11.7 Case study – Data post-processing

An anemometer device for measuring wind speed and direction consists of a pole which bends in the wind and has strain gauges attached to it to give an indication of the degree of bending in the N-S and E-W directions (Figure 11.1). The strain gauges are connected to amplifiers and analogue-to-digital converters which give an output for each of the axes of 1 unit per 0.8 km/h of wind speed component. This means that we have two numbers which represent the N-S component (southern values being negative) and the E-W component (west being negative). These two values are sampled every second for a whole day and stored in a file which for this example is called *wind.dat*. Our job is to write a program to post-process this data and convert it to a file containing the average speed of the wind

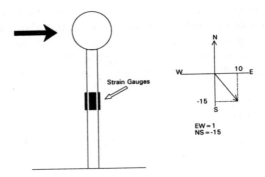

Figure 11.1 Strain gauge anemometer

for every ten minute interval. The raw data therefore appears in a file as shown below (note that each record occupies a line with a newline character \n to indicate the end of the line).

wind.dat

```
34    -23\n
36    -23\n
36    -18\n
37    -20\n
36    -20\n
37    -30\n
 .     .
 .     .
 .     .
[EOF]
```

This file will contain 86400 entries. We calculate the wind speed by taking the magnitude of the vector that each set of numbers represents (i.e. use Pythagoras). For example, the first two figures represent a wind speed of:

$$\sqrt{(34*0.8)^2+(-23*0.8)^2} = 32.8 \text{ km/h}$$

The resulting processed data is written to a file specified by the user. The main program is as follows:

```
#include <stdio.h>
#include <math.h>
#define NSAMPLES 86400
#define AVERAGE_SET_SIZE 60
#define CONVERSION_FACTOR 0.8
FILE *datafile, *resultfile;
```

```
main ()
{
  int error_code;

  /* Open files */
  opendatafile ();
  openresultfile ();

  /* Process file. Returns 1 if ok or 0 if error */
  error_code=process ();

  if (error_code==0) printf ("Error in data file");
          else   printf ("Finished OK.");

  fclose (datafile);
  fclose (resultfile);
}
```

The *#define* directives define constants for the conversion factor (i.e. km/h per unit step of the A-D convertor), the number of samples expected in the file (i.e. one per second for 24 hours) and the size of the set of samples used in the averaging process (i.e. 60 samples for one minute). Two *FILE* pointer variables are defined for the input and output files. These are defined globally, so that they may be used by all functions. These could (and preferably should) be defined local to the *main* function, but we are then required to use techniques involving pointer variables to indicate to functions what files to use. This will be covered in the next chapter.

The *main* program simply calls functions to open the files and then calls the function *process* to read the data, process it and write it back out. This function returns a value indicating if any error occurred (e.g. wrong number of samples in the file).

The function to open the data file is given below:

```
void opendatafile (void)
{
  char filename [50];

  do
  {
    printf ("Input file name of data file");
    scanf ("%s", filename);
    datafile=fopen (filename, "r");
    if (datafile==NULL)
    {
      printf ("\n\a Error. Could not open file\n");
    }
  }
  while (datafile==NULL);
}
```

This reads in a string for the filename and attempts to open this file for reading. If unsuccessful (e.g. file does not exist), then the loop executes, giving the user another opportunity to enter the filename. The global file pointer variable *datafile* should then be set to the appropriate file of data on exit. The function *openresultfile* is virtually identical, but opens a file for writing and sets the variable *resultfile*.

The function to process the data can be written as follows in terms of pseudocode:

```
for each sample in file
{
  read NS and EW value
  apply conversion factor to convert to km/s
  calculate velocity
  add velocity to running total
  each time 60 samples read
  {
    calculate average velocity for the minute
    write result to file
    reset running total
  }
}
```

After refinement, this produces the following code:

```
int process(void)
{
  int sample, n, readcode;
  float speed, speedsum, NS,EW;

  sample=0; speedsum=0;

  for (sample=1;sample<=NSAMPLES;sample++)
  {
    /* Read NS and EW components */
    readcode=fscanf(datafile,"%f %f",&NS,&EW);

    /* Test values read OK. If not terminate */
    if (readcode!=2) return 0;

    /*Calc. speed. First apply conversion factor */
    NS=NS*CONVERSION_FACTOR;
    EW=EW*CONVERSION_FACTOR;
    speed=sqrt(NS*NS+EW*EW);

    /* Add to running total for minute */
    speedsum=speedsum+speed;

    /* Test if all samples for minute are read */
    if (sample%AVERAGE_SET_SIZE==0)
```

```
{
    /* Samples for minute read. Write to file */
    speed=speedsum/AVERAGE_SET_SIZE;
    fprintf(resultfile,"%5.1f ",speed);

    /* reset summation variable */
    speedsum=0;
}
}
/* If at this point then all is OK */
return 1;
}
```

This loops for a number of iterations indicated by *Nsample* under the control of the variable *sample*. Each time around the loop, two values are read from the data file into the variables *NS* and *EW*, which represent the two components of the wind vector. The value returned by *fscanf* should be two, to indicate that two values were successfully read. If this is not the case, then the file has an error in it and so the function terminates with the appropriate return value.

If the values are read correctly then the speed is calculated and added to running totals, so that an average can be taken.

The next section tests if it is time to take an average and write it out. This means testing if we have summed another 60 samples. If this is true, then the average speed is calculated and is written to the output file. The summation variable is set to 0 and the loop then continues until all the expected data has been read.

11.8   Summary

- Files can be written or read using the *fprintf* and *fscanf* functions which are similar in operation to *printf* and *scanf*.

- Files must be opened before any read or write operation can take place. This is done using the *fopen* function which identifies the file on the file system (creating it if necessary) and returns a value of type *FILE*, which can be assigned to a variable, which can then be used as a reference to the file.

- When opening a file, a special value denoted by the constant *NULL* may be returned by *fopen*. This denotes that the file could not be opened, usually because no file with the name specified was found, or because the file is in read-only mode.

- When a file is finished with, it can be closed using the *fclose* function. Files are automatically closed on program termination.

• When reading a file, *fscanf* will return a special value identified as *EOF* to indicate that a read past the end of the file has been attempted.

11.9   Exercises

1) Write a program which produces a file of 1000 random integer numbers between −10000 and +10000.

2) Write a program to read in 1000 integer numbers into an array and then print their mean, median, mode and largest (most positive) value. To find the mode is very difficult and you should not resort to using any extra large arrays. Instead, sort the array into order. It can then be scanned and the longest sequence of a single value found.

3) Write a program which reads in a C program from a file and produces an output file which is the same program with any comments removed. The file can be read a character at a time, so there is no need for large arrays. The names of the files should be user specified and a checks should be made to ensure that input and output files do not have the same names.

12 Pointers

12.1 Introduction

For all the programs we have seen so far we have used simple variables which are adequate for most simple programming tasks. However, for more advanced applications it can become more convenient to use pointer type variables since they offer flexibility, allow faster code to be created, and also allow new variables to be created as necessary as the program is running. We will not go into great detail of the more esoteric techniques which become possible through using pointers. Instead, we will introduce the basic concepts and illustrate some simpler techniques which will be sufficient for present purposes.

12.2 Pointer concepts

We are familiar with variable definitions such as:

```
int value;
```

This will create a single variable (probably two bytes in length) somewhere in memory which will contain an integer value. We refer to this area of memory using the identifier '*value*' in assignments and expressions, as we have seen in most of the examples we have looked at until now. A pointer is also a variable, but rather than containing a value such as an integer, character or floating point number, it contains a memory address. The address contained in the pointer will generally be that of some data in memory (i.e. the address of an 'ordinary' variable). Therefore, the contents of a pointer can 'point' at some other variable in memory where some data can be found.

12.3 Defining pointers

To create a pointer variable we define the variable in a similar way to defining other variables. A generalised definition is shown below:

```
type_identifier *variable_identifier;
```

We first have a type identifier (e.g. *int, float*) which indicates the type of value to which the pointer will point. Then follows the variable identifier (i.e. name) which is prefixed with an asterisk (*) to indicate that it is a pointer variable. A typical definition might be:

```
int   *valuep;
```

This creates a variable called *valuep* which can be used to point to an integer value in memory. We will, as a rule, add a '*p*' to the names of pointer variables if the name does not obviously imply that it is a pointer. This is not a requirement of the C language. Another definition might be:

```
double *another_valuep;
```

This creates a variable containing a memory address which can point to a *double* type value in memory. Note that the size of a pointer variable is determined by the number of bytes required to hold a memory address on the machine on which the program will run. Therefore, all pointers are the same size, no matter what type of value they point to (e.g. a pointer to an *int* is the same size as a pointer to a *double*). You may start to wonder why we need to associate a type with a pointer since all pointers have the same structure. The reason is for type checking and conversions. We must know what representation is used in storing the value to which a pointer is pointing, so that type conversions can be performed when evaluating expressions, etc. Therefore, a *float* type pointer is only used for pointing to *float* type values, and an *int* type pointer is only used for pointing at *int* type values. Even though each type of pointer has the same structure, we should not end up misinterpreting a value stored, thanks to the type associated with the pointer.

12.4   The & operator

We have so far stated that a pointer is a variable which contains the memory address of another variable. To be able to assign a value to a pointer, it is sometimes necessary to find the address of a variable. This is done using the & operator. Consider the following variable definition:

```
int value;
```

This causes a space of memory to be reserved which is large enough to hold an integer value (usually two bytes). The precise location in memory where the variable is placed is decided by the linker and is usually of no consequence to the programmer who simply refers to the variable by its identifier. However, if we require the memory address of the variable, then the following expression will evaluate to this:

```
&value
```

Consider this in a detailed example. The definition below creates and initialises the variable *temp* to 25.6 and let us assume that the linker chooses to locate the variable in memory starting at the location with address 10500. The variable is of type *float* and we will assume that it occupies four bytes on the system in use.

float temp=25.6;

The memory in this region will appear as follows:

```
                        |                 |  10506
                        |        ?        |  10505
                        |        ?        |  10504
                        |                 |  10503
                        |      25.6       |  10502
                        |    (4 bytes     |  10501
            temp>       |     long)       |  10500
                        |        ?        |  10499
                        |        ?        |  10498
                        |                 |  10497
```

We have an area starting from address 10500 which is four bytes long and contains the floating point representation of the value 25.6. Therefore, the expression below will evaluate to 25.6:

`temp`

whereas the next expression evaluates to the address of the variable (10500):

`&temp`

12.5 Assigning pointers

We can assign the values of two pointers just as we can assign the values of other variables. Consider the following definitions:

```
int a, *point1;
float x, *point2, *point3;
```

This creates an integer variable *a*, a pointer to an integer called *point1*, a floating point variable *x*, and two pointers to *float* type variables called *point2* and *point3*. We can now make the following assignments to the pointers:

```
point1=&a;
point2=&x;
```

This now means that the pointer variable *point1* contains the memory address of the integer variable *a* and the pointer *point2* contains the memory address of the *float* variable *x*. Now let us consider some more assignments:

```
point3=point2;
```

This is a valid assignment and the result is that the value in *point2* is copied to *point3*. Since *point2* contains the memory address of the variable *x*, then *point3* will also now be pointing to the variable *x*. We have therefore assigned a memory address from one pointer to another. Consider similar examples such as:

```
point3=point1;
point3=&a;
```

The first assignment assigns the contents of *point1* (which is the memory address of integer variable *a*) to the pointer *point3*. Although this seems similar to the previous example, the compiler will flag an error or warning. The reason is that *point3* was defined as a pointer to a *float* type value, but we are attempting here to point it at an *int* type value. The compiler will detect this, but may still compile the program, so beware! Generally, if this sort of situation occurs, it means that the program design needs to be reviewed as it is flawed. The second assignment is another example of the same situation.

12.6   Pointer indirection

We have seen how to assign the value of pointers to each other. However, a more normal use of pointers is to access the data to which they actually point. This is done by a process called indirection. Consider the following definitions:

```
int x=23;
int *xaddressp;
```

This creates an integer variable called *x*, which is initialised to the value 23, and a pointer to an integer called *xaddressp*. Then assume that we execute the following statement:

```
xaddressp=&x;
```

This now means that the pointer variable *xaddressp* contains the address of variable *x*. This means that we can now refer to the variable *x* in two ways. Firstly, we can simply quote its identifier as we have done before. For example:

```
printf("%i",x);
```

This will print the value 23 on the screen. Alternatively, we can refer to the variable *x* via the pointer *xaddressp*. If we prefix the pointer name with an asterisk, the compiler interprets this as an indication that we are referring to the value that the pointer is pointing to, and not the value of the pointer itself. For example:

```
printf("%i",*xaddressp);
```

This also prints 23 and is interpreted as 'print the integer value found at the address stored in the pointer variable *xaddressp*'. Hence the use of the term indirection, since we are referring to the variable *x* indirectly, via its memory address which is stored in a pointer. We can manipulate variable *x* indirectly in all the same ways as we have done using direct references. For example:

```
x=34;
```

is exactly equivalent to:

```
*xaddressp=34;
```

assuming that *xaddressp* has been set to point to variable *x*.

This mode of use of pointers has no great advantages over the direct addressing of variables. However, the power of pointers becomes more apparent when dealing with parameters and return values of functions, which we shall examine shortly.

12.7 Self-assessment test − Pointers

What values are printed by the following program?:

```
main()
{
  int a, b, *pi1, *pi2;
  float x, y, *pf1, *pf2;

  a=2;
  b=3;
```

```
    x=3.5;
    pil=&a;
    pi2=pil;
    printf("%i",*pi2);        /* a */
    pil=&b;
    a=*pil+*pi2;
    printf("%i",a);           /* b */
    pf1=&x;
    *pf1=*pf1-1;
    printf("%f",x);           /* c */
    *pil=*pil**pf1;
    printf("%i",b);           /* d */
}
```

Answers: a) Pointer *pi2* points to variable *a* and so the value 2 is printed.
b)   *pil* is set to point at variable *b*, *pil* points to variable *a* and so the line
a=*pil+pi2; is equivalent to *a=b+a;* which results in a value of 5 in variable
a which is printed.   c) *pf1* points to variable *x* which contains 3.5. The line
*pf1=*pf1−1; is therefore equivalent to *x=x−1;* which results in the value of
2.5 being placed in *x* which is then printed.   d) *pil* points to variable *b* which
contains 3 and *pf1* points to variable *x* which contains 2.5. The line
*pil=*pil**pf1; is therefore equivalent to *b=b*x;*. This involves type
conversions and so the integer value 3 will be converted to a *float* for the
calculation, which results in a value of 7.5. This is assigned to an *int* type
variable and so the fractional part is truncated. The final value printed is
therefore 7.

12.8   *NULL* pointers

There is a special value which a pointer can assume in order to indicate that it
is not pointing at anything. This value is identified with the word *NULL*. We can
assign this to a pointer (in this example called *ptrp*) as follows:

```
ptrp=NULL;
```

If this pointer is now used as a reference to a value using the indirection
operator (i.e. *) then a run-time error may occur and the program may terminate
with an error message (note that not all compilers produce code which checks
for this situation).

The most common use of the *NULL* value is when using functions which
return a pointer type value (more on this later). Often, if the function fails to
complete its task for some reason, it returns the value *NULL* to indicate that an
error has occurred. An example of this is the function *calloc*, which is used to
request additional memory space while a program is running. It returns a pointer
value which indicates the start of the memory block allocated. However, if there

is insufficient memory available, then the returned value is *NULL*. To detect this we might have the following section of code:

```
int *ptrp;
ptrp=calloc(4,8);
if (ptrp==NULL)
{
  printf("Could not allocate memory");
  exit(0);
}
```

In this example we call *calloc* with two arguments which determines the size of the block of memory required (we are not too concerned with the details of this function here). The function then returns the memory address of the start of the memory block assigned or, if there is insufficient memory, a value of *NULL* is returned. We then test the value which is stored in the pointer variable *ptrp* which, if found to be *NULL*, causes the program to terminate with an appropriate message, otherwise the program continues and we can use the memory through the address in *ptrp*. Do not worry too much about the use of the function *calloc* here, it is simply used as an example of a function which returns a pointer value. Another example is the *fopen* function used to open a file. If used to open a non-existent file for reading, the value *NULL* is returned to indicate that there is a problem.

12.9   Pointers as parameters

We have seen many examples of functions in which a number of arguments in a function call are copied to the parameter variables which are local to the function being called. For many situations this is sufficient, as it also isolates variables in one area of the program from other areas, which is often desirable. However, there are cases where this isolation is unhelpful and so we can get around this by using pointers. Take the following example, which is a program to swap the contents of two variables:

```
void swap(int a, int b)
{
  int temp;   /* Temporary storage */

  temp=a;
  a=b;
  b=temp;
}
```

We might call this function from the main program, using two integer variables as arguments called *x* and *y*:

```
x=5;
y=8;
swap(x,y);
```

When the *swap* function is first called the values of the arguments are copied to the parameter variables which are local to the function. Therefore, as *swap* begins executing the variables appear as follows (the variable *temp* is omitted as its use is incidental):

<table>
<tr><td>main function</td><td>swap function</td></tr>
<tr><td>x</td><td>a</td></tr>
<tr><td>5</td><td>5</td></tr>
<tr><td>y</td><td>b</td></tr>
<tr><td>8</td><td>8</td></tr>
</table>

At the end of the swap function the variables will have the following values (before the variables *a* and *b* are lost on return from the function):

<table>
<tr><td>main function</td><td>swap function</td></tr>
<tr><td>x</td><td>a</td></tr>
<tr><td>5</td><td>8</td></tr>
<tr><td>y</td><td>b</td></tr>
<tr><td>8</td><td>5</td></tr>
</table>

Notice that the values of *a* and *b* are interchanged, but on return the function has not affected variables *x* and *y*; all we have done is swap copies of *x* and *y* around and then discard these copies which is of no use at all. This isolation between arguments and parameters is good in that it means that if we use a function which we know little about, we can be sure that it will not affect the variables that are used as arguments, but simply only make copies of them. However, if we specifically want a function to swap the values of two variables used as arguments, then this mechanism will not allow this. Instead we must pass as arguments the addresses of the variables. The swap function now becomes

```
void swap(int *ap, int *bp)
{
  int temp;
  temp=*ap;
  *ap=*bp;
  *bp=temp;
}
```

To call this function, we now write:

```
swap(&x,&y);
```

Notice that the parameter variables are now pointer type variables and receive the address of the argument variables in the main program called *x* and *y*. Therefore, when the function is called, **a* is a reference to variable of *x* of the *main* function, and **b* is a reference to variable *y*. Therefore, when we now swap the values referenced by **a* and **b*, we are actually swapping the contents of the original variables *x* and *y*, rather than copies of *x* and *y* as before. The consequences of this are summarised below:

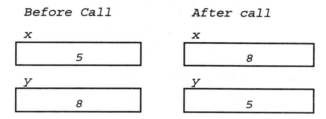

Another good example of this is the *scanf* function, which loads a variable with a value corresponding to the user's input. Consider a call of *scanf* such as:

```
scanf("%i",&n);
```

This call has two arguments, the first of which is a string which tells *scanf* how to interpret the input (i.e. convert it to *int* type representation). The second argument is an address at which the value produced by *scanf* will be placed. We must therefore give *scanf* the address of an integer variable so that the value appears in the variable on return. This is why the & operator is used.

12.10 Arrays as parameters

When passing arrays as parameters we have already stated that it would be very time consuming to create a new array as the function begins, into which we copy all the arguments from the original argument array. Instead, the value passed to the receiving function is simply the memory address of the start of the array. Therefore, the array used as an argument, and the array referred to by the function, will be physically the same array. This is the same in concept as passing pointers as arguments, as we have already seen. To understand this more fully, we must look again at array definitions. Consider the following:

```
int   value_list[5]={7,4,23,9,12};
```

This sets up a ten-element array of integers. Now consider the following expressions:

```
value_list[2]
value_list[0]
value_list
```

The first of these evaluates to the value stored in the third element of the array (23), and the next expression evaluates to the value stored in the first element of the array (7). These are simply integer expressions, as we have seen many times. However, the third expression does not refer to any specific element of the array, and in this case this evaluates to the memory address of the first element of the array in memory. Therefore, to find the position of the beginning of an array (including strings) in memory we do not need to use the & operator; instead we just quote the array identifier without a subscript.

To illustrate this, we will write a function to take the square root of all the values in an array. In our main program we might have the following definition:

```
int number_list[10]={4,6,42,66,78,3,4,25,12,98};
```

This creates an array of ten values called *number_list*. We now call a function called *root_all* to find all their square roots:

```
root_all(number_list, 10);
```

The function *root_all* requires as an argument the address of the beginning of the array. In this case this is the value of *number_list* with no subscript. We also need to tell the function how long the array is, because the function has no way of knowing this from just a memory address. Therefore, a second integer parameter is used for this. The definition of the function *root_all* will be:

```
void root_all(int list[], int length)
{
  int n;
  for (n=0;n<length;n++)
  {
    list[n]=sqrt(list[n]);
  }
}
```

The first parameter here is a pointer variable called *list*, which receives the address of the start of the array. Notice that it is defined as an array, but in reality it is simply a pointer and it would be quite valid to replace *int list[ ]* with *int *list*. The two are exactly equivalent, but the first is preferable in this case, as it clearly indicates that we are dealing with an array and not a pointer to a single variable.

The second parameter is a simple integer which is the array length. The function now executes a loop, which allows us to step through the array, using *n* as an index which is incremented at each cycle. We refer to each element of the array as:

```
list[n];
```

This takes the address in the pointer variable called *list* and adds to this the correct number to get to the address of the *n*th element. So if *n* is 0, then this simply evaluates to the value of *list*, which already points to the first element. If *n* is 2 then this evaluates to *list+4* to obtain the address of the third element (remember, memory addresses go up one per byte, and an *int* variable usually occupies 2 bytes, but the compiler will take care of this sort of thing anyway).

Therefore, after calling the function *root_all*, the original array *number_list* will contain the following value, all rounded down to integers:

```
2 2 6 8 8 12 5 2 9
```

Another example is a function to convert a string to upper case. Suppose that we have the following definition and function call:

```
char    myname[5]="Fred";

str_toupper(myname);
```

This creates a string containing *"Fred\0"*, where \0 is the string terminator character. We pass the address of this array to the function *str_toupper*, which converts all letters to upper case in the argument string. This function has the following form:

```
void str_toupper(char str[])
{
  int n;

  n=0;
  while (str[n]!='\0')
  {
    str[n]=toupper(str[n]);
    n++;
  }
}
```

This function simply extracts each of the characters in turn from the array and converts them to upper case, using the standard function *toupper* which works on single characters. Notice that this function does not require us to pass a separate argument which is the length of the array, since there should be a string terminator character before the end of the array. This marks the end of the string, so the function can end when it is encountered. The original array *myname* will now contain "*FRED\0*".

12.11 Pointers as return values

We have seen how functions can return values such as single integer or floating point values. A function can also return a pointer value. An example is illustrated below. The function *biggest* below finds the largest value in the array passed to it and returns the memory address of that value.

```
float *biggest(float array[],int size)
{
  int n;
  float largest, *largestp;

  largest=array[0];
  largestp=&array[n];

  for (n=0;n<size;n++)
  {
    if (array[n]>largest)
    {
      largest=array[n];
      largestp=&array[n];
    }
  }
  return largestp;
}
```

This function simply starts by assuming that the first element of the array is the largest and notes the value and addresses of this element in the variables *largest* and *largestp*. It then scans the rest of the array and, if a larger value is found, then the variables *largest* and *largestp* are updated to the value and address of this new element of the array. On completion, the value in *largestp* will be the address of the largest element in the array, which is then returned. Note the use of the * symbol in the first line of the function to indicate that it returns the address of a *float* type variable (i.e. it returns a pointer value).

To call this function we might write:

```
float value_table[8]={2.3,4.5,0.4,3,6.7,8,3,2.1};
float *bigp;

bigp=biggest(value_table,8);
printf("Biggest value is %f",*bigp);
```

Here we pass the function the address of an 8-element array of *float* and the length of the array as a separate argument. The returned address is then assigned to the pointer *bigp*, which can then be used as a reference to this array element.

The example above could also be written by simply returning a float value equal to the largest element of the array, so returning a pointer may not offer real advantages here. However, if we have a function in which we want to return something other than a single value, such as an array or a structure (which we will examine later), then C does not allow this. The compiler will only allow simple types to be used as return values. To get around this, we can return a pointer to the array or structure from the function allowing access to the functions results. We will not look at this in any great detail here, but will come across it in later chapters.

12.12 Absolute addressing

It is often the case that we want to access a specific memory location in an engineering application which might for example be a memory-mapped peripheral device (i.e. a hardware device 'pretending' to be a normal memory location). The way this is done is to create a pointer of the most suitable type to be able to manipulate the types of values read or written to the memory location and then assign to this pointer the appropriate address. We can the access the memory location through the pointer, using indirection.

As an example, let us suppose that we have an 8-bit parallel output port, which communicates to a printer at location 0x0045 in memory (note the use of hexadecimal format usually used for addresses, although this is not a requirement). To write to this printer, we will send out characters which are 8-bit ASCII codes that the printer can recognise and print. Therefore, we can make the following pointer definition:

```
char *printerportp;
```

This sets up a pointer which can point to an 8-bit character 'variable' in memory. We must now point this pointer to the correct address, so that we can make the assignment:

```
printerportp=0x0045;
```

This may not work in some implementations since, strictly speaking, we are assigning an integer constant to a pointer, both of which are of different types (i.e. use different representations). Therefore, it may be necessary to use a type cast to convert the integer constant to a 'pointer to a character' type value:

```
printerportp=(char *)0x0045;
```

To write a character to the printer, we can then write:

```
*printerportp='A';
```

The ASCII value for 'A' is sent to this memory location which, so far as C is concerned, is a normal memory location. In reality, this is a hardware device which passes the value on to the printer.

This is in principle how to achieve this kind of task. However, this is non-standard C, and it is best to refer to your compiler documentation for more detail. One important case to note is that of addressing on IBM PC compatible machines. The memory of these machines is organised slightly differently to other machines, in that it consists of blocks of memory called segments, each of which is 64 kbytes long. When addressing a memory location, we must specify which segment we are concerned with and the position within that segment of the location (the offset). Therefore, a memory address consists of two 16-bit parts, a segment address and an offset.

The situation is further complicated in that there are two types of pointer available, called *near* and *far* pointers. Since a compiler tends to store all variables in one area, it is common for them to be contained in a single segment. Therefore, to access these variables, we only need to remember the offset address of each, provided that a note has been made somewhere of the start of the segment containing the data. This cuts down processing time and halves the size of pointer variables to 16 bits. However, as a consequence we cannot address anything outside the 64k segment.

For our purposes, the second type of pointer called a *far* pointer is more useful, because it stores the segment and offset address. It can therefore access any area of memory, but as a consequence it is 32 bits in length and takes longer to process. The structure of a *far* pointer is as follows:

Segment Address	Offset
(16-bit value)	(16-bit value)

As an example, we will look at a program which displays the time of day. This is possible since the operating system increments a 32-bit value in memory every 18.2 seconds (assuming that the MS-DOS operating system is in use). This value is set to 0 at midnight, so from this we can calculate the time of day. The address of the memory location is 0x0040 for the segment and 0x006c for the offset. Also note that the 32-bit simple binary value representing the time has the same format as a *long int* in most implementations. Therefore, to access this address, we define the following pointer:

```
long int far *ptrp;
```

Note the use of the extra *far* type specifier, which indicates that we want this to be a *far* pointer which can point to any point in memory, as opposed to a *near* pointer which is limited to 64k in the data segment. We now need to assign to this pointer the correct address, so we write:

```
ptrp=(long int far *) 0x0040006c;
```

Note the type cast used here to change the integer constant to a memory address of a *long int*, using a *far* type address. The variable *ptrp* now appears in memory as:

Segment Address	Offset
0x0040	0x006c

Note that we have had to combine the segment and offset to form the value 0x0040006c which when assigned to the pointer gives us the correct values in the two halves of the pointer. This is done simply by multiplying the segment address by 2^{16} (or 0x10000) and adding the offset to this. To obtain the number of seconds elapsed since midnight, we can now write:

```
time=*ptrp/18.2;
```

This reads the contents of the appropriate address and divides it by 18.2 (N.B. the value is converted to floating point for the calculation). The result is assigned to an integer variable called *time*. This value can then be converted to three values, for hours, minutes and seconds, using a few arithmetic operations. The complete program is as follows:

```
#include <stdio.h>

main()
{
  long int time,far *ptrp;
  long int hours,minutes,seconds;

  ptrp=(long int far *) 0x40006c;

  time=*ptrp/18.2;
  hours=time/3600;
  time=time-hours*3600;
  minutes=time/60;
  time=time-minutes*60;
  seconds=time;
  printf("%li:%li:%li\n",hours,minutes,seconds);
}
```

The result is a display of the time in the form:

```
12:34:56
```

The details of this program will change from one implementation to another, as much of this is non-standard. The reader is recommended to consult the documentation for the compiler in use before attempting this type of programming.

12.13 Self-assessment test — Pointer parameters

Here is a function which rounds a floating point value to the nearest integer value. To round to the nearest value, we add 0.5 and then truncate the fractional parts; for example, 4.4 plus 0.5 becomes 4.9, which truncated is 4. However, 4.6 plus 0.5 becomes 5.1, which truncated is 5. The function accepts two arguments, one being the value to be rounded, and the other being the address of an integer variable where the rounded value is to be stored.

```
void round(float x, int *result)
{
  x=x+0.5;
  *result=x
}
```

For each of the following calls we assume the existence of a *float* type variable y, which contains the value 4.7 and an *int* variable n. Which calls are valid and, if they are valid, what is the effect of the call?

```
round(y,&n);      /* a */
round(y,n);       /* b */
round(6.6,&n);    /* c */
round(8,&n);      /* d */
round(y,8);       /* e */
```

Answers: a) Valid. Results in the value 5 being assigned to n. b) Invalid. The second argument evaluates to the contents of variable n, which is an *int* type value. The function expects a memory address instead.   c) Valid. The value of 7 is assigned to n. d) Valid. 8 is assigned to n.   e) Invalid. The second argument must be the address of a variable. The constant '8' has no associated address.

12.14 Summary

- A pointer is a variable which points to a value in memory (i.e. contains a memory address of another variable).

- Pointers can be assigned or tested for equality in the same manner as other variables. Assigning a value to a pointer means setting the memory address that it contains (i.e. pointing it to a particular place in memory).

- The value to which a pointer is pointing is accessed through the pointer, using the indirection operator.

- A variable accessed through pointer indirection can be used in the same way as any other variable.

- The & operator can be used to refer to the memory address of a variable. The result can be assigned to a pointer directly, or by using it as a function call argument.

- Pointer parameters can be used to allow variables that would otherwise be local to one function, to be accessed by other functions. They also allow references to large structured variables to be passed, without a large degree of copying being performed.

- References to arrays without subscripts yields the address of the start of the array. This can be assigned to a pointer, usually as a function argument.

- Some compilers allow the user to set a pointer using an absolute address for accessing hardware, etc. This is not standard, but is often useful in engineering applications.

Note that there are a many techniques which become possible when using pointers. We have only scratched the surface of this area, but the reader should now have a sufficient grasp of the subject for present purposes.

12.15 Exercises

1) Using the *swap* function of section 12.9, write a bubble sort function to sort an array of numbers into order. The array entries are to be swapped using the *swap* function.

2) Write a program which reads in a sentence of words separated by spaces. The program should print out just the second word. To do this, read the string into a string variable and pass it to a function, defined as:

```
char *second_word(char str[])
```

This function scans the string for the second word (i.e. looks at spaces) and then returns a pointer which is the address of the start of the second word. A function, defined as follows, can then be called and be passed this address:

```
void printword(char *word)
```

or

```
void printword(char word[])
```

The two definitions are equivalent. This function should then print the second word of the sentence on the monitor.

3) A sorting program to sort a list of N values in an array can be written in pseudocode as follows:

```
for all elements in part of array not sorted
{
    find largest value and note position
    swap largest value with top value in unsorted part
        of array
}
```

Therefore, if we have ten values we scan all ten, note the position of largest and then swap it with the top element of the array. We then repeat the process on the remaining nine elements of the array, so that the largest value of those remaining is placed at the top of these nine elements. Then we continue with the remaining eight, and so on. The result is eventually a sorted array. Write a program to implement this, using the *swap* function mentioned in exercise 1. To find the largest element of the array, use a function of the form:

```
int *largest(int values[], int n)
```

where *values[ ]* is a pointer to the start of the unsorted section of the array and *n* is the number of values in this unsorted section. The return value is a pointer to the largest value found.

13 Advanced Data Types

13.1   Introduction

We have previously seen how C represents various items of data according to
the type of that data (e.g. integers, floats and characters). These simple data
types form the basis of all data representation in C programs, but it is not always
convenient or logical to use variables of these types individually. For example,
to store a person's details (name, address and phone number) could be done
using a number of individual variables of string and integer types, but this
quickly leads to difficulties if the details of many people are to be processed. We
will examine in this chapter how C allows us to group variables of different
types, in order to create structured variables to hold more complex data.

13.2   The concept of structures

Consider a system which maintains the stock records for a small electronics
store. Components are stored in numbered bins. The system must keep track of
the following data for each stock item:

Component Type	(e.g. "Resistor", "Transistor")
Component ID	(e.g. "NE555", "BC107")
Component Value	(e.g. 10000 Ω, 0.1 μf)
Bin Number	(e.g. 0..2000)
Number in stock	(e.g. 0..2000)

We could represent this data as 5 separate variables of type array of *char*,
array of *char*, *float*, *int* and *int*, respectively. This would be quite acceptable for
a program which only processed data for a single stock item, but we will be
dealing with many thousands of such items. It is much more convenient from the
programmer's point of view to have a type of variable which can hold all the
information for a stock item in one identifiable 'box'. This is possible in C using
the concept of structures. The structure required for the stock system will still
contain 5 separate variables as already listed, but these variables of differing
types are to be gathered up into a single logical unit to hold all the information
for a particular stock item.

13.3   Declaring new types

We are already familiar with the concept of variable type. When storing an item of data, we select a type of variable suitable for the nature of that data (e.g. we use an `int` type variable to store the number of rooms in a house, a *float* to store the cosine of an angle, and a `char` to store which key on the keyboard has been hit). The names of these simple types (*int, float, char, double,* etc.) are already known by the C compiler, and the compiler acts appropriately when it encounters them. However, we cannot use these types of variable to hold more complex data which may consist of several parts, each of which may need a different type of variable to store it, as in our stock control example. To get around this problem, C allows us to define new types of variable, specifically designed for the data that it is to hold. This process consists of a type declaration, which assigns a name to our new type and sets down the sort of data that any variable of this type can hold. Note that a type declaration does not create a variable (i.e. no memory is set aside to hold data). All we are doing is making a statement about the nature of any variables that are created using this new type. The use of this idea should become clearer as you read through the chapter.

13.4   Declaring a structure

The most usual way to use structures is first to declare a new data type. Once this type is declared, we can use it when we define variables, just as we have done when we defined variables with simple types. For our stock control system we can declare a new type called *StockItem*, as follows:

```
struct StockItem
{
  char   ComponentType[10];
  char   ComponentID[10];
  float  ComponentValue;
  int    Bin Number;
  int    NumberInStock;
};
```

Notice that we have not actually created a variable (i.e. no 'box' in memory has been reserved for data), as this is a declaration, not a definition. What we have stated is that any subsequent variable defined as type *StockItem* will actually consist of five parts, two strings, a float and two integers. We have created a template of how a variable is structured, without creating any actual variables.

The declaration of a structure begins with the word *struct*, followed by an identifier which in this case has been chosen to be the word *StockItem*. Then, in braces, there follows a list of the component parts of the structure with types and identifiers.

13.5 Defining structured variables

Once we have declared a structure type, we can then define variables of this new type. Let us assume that we need to store the details of one of our stock items (say a capacitor) in a variable named *ThisComponent*. We define *ThisComponent* as follows:

```
struct   StockItem   ThisComponent;
```

We can contrast this with a definition of an integer variable (called *singleInt*), with which we are already familiar. This definition would take the form

```
int SingleInt;
```

In this case the type is *int*, as opposed to *struct StockItem*, and the variable name is *SingleInt*, as opposed to *ThisComponent*. Notice that when quoting a structured type we precede the structure name with the keyword *struct*.

Our declaration of the variables *SingleInt* and *ThisComponent* can be easily contrasted by representing them graphically as physical boxes, to represent the areas of memory which are reserved for the data to be stored.

```
SingleInt                                        ThisComponent
┌──────────────┐                                ┌──────────────┐
│ (int value)  │        ComponentType           │ (string)     │
└──────────────┘        ComponentID             ├──────────────┤
                        ComponentValue          │ (string)     │
                        BinNumber               ├──────────────┤
                        NumberInStock           │ (float value)│
                                                ├──────────────┤
                                                │ (int value)  │
                                                ├──────────────┤
                                                │ (int value)  │
                                                └──────────────┘
```

If required, we can define many variables as type *StockItem*. We can also initialise them at the same time as defining them, as shown in the following example:

```
struct StockItem a,b,c={"TRANSISTOR","BC107",0.0,
                        112,78};
```

This creates three variables of type *StockItem*, the first two of which are uninitialised (*a* and *b*), and the third (called *c*) is initialised to represent the contents of bin 112, which are BC107 transistors, of which there are 78 in stock. The 0.0 is the component value which is not really applicable to transistors but is used for such things as resistors and capacitors. The order of initialisation is determined by the order in which the components of the structure are declared.

The variable *c* will appear as shown in memory following this definition:

	c
ComponentType	*"Transistor"*
ComponentID	*"BC107"*
ComponentValue	*0.0*
BinNumber	*112*
NumberInStock	*78*

13.6   Accessing structure members

Any variable defined as type *StockItem* will consist of five separate parts, which we will refer to as members of the structure. Each of these members is given an identifier (a tag) when the structure type is declared (e.g. *ComponentType*, *ComponentValue*, etc.). We may access the individual members of any variable defined as this type by quoting the variable name, followed by the member tag, with a dot to separate. For example:

```
struct StockItem
{
  char   ComponentType[10];
  char   ComponentID[10];
  float  ComponentValue;
  int    BinNumber;
  int    NumberInStock;
};

main ()
{
  struct StockItem ComponentA={"RESISTOR","",1000,
                      314, 68};
  struct StockItem ComponentB={"DIODE","1N4001",
                      0.0,13,32};
  struct StockItem Z;

  ComponentA.BinNumber=33;
  ComponentB.NumberInStock--;

  scanf("%f",&ComponentA.ComponentValue);

  Z=ComponentB;
  printf("We have %i of %s %s in stock",
          Z.NumberInStock, Z.ComponentID,
          Z.ComponentType);
}
```

In this program we have declared a structured type called *StockItem*. Notice that this is outside the *main* function and so is known globally (i.e. other following functions can have variables defined as *StockItem*). At the beginning of our program we define three variables *ComponentA, ComponentB* and *Z* to be of type *StockItem*. The variable *ComponentA* is also initialised to represent the content of bin 314 to be 1 k resistors, of which we have 68. *ComponentB* is initialised to represent the 32 diodes (type 1n4001) in bin 13. Variable *Z* is uninitialised.

If we were to move the contents of bin 68 to bin 33, then the next line of code takes account of this (N.B. it is very unlikely that this is how it would be coded in reality, this is purely an illustration). We therefore set the *BinNumber* member of *ComponentA* to 33. In fact, *ComponentA.BinNumber* is simply an integer variable and can be treated in the same manner as any other integer variable.

If we were to take an 1n4001 diode from the stores then we would need to reduce the appropriate record, which is held in *ComponentB*. This is achieved in the next line, which decrements the *NumberInStock* member by one.

If we needed to change the value of the resistors whose details are stored in *ComponentA*, this could be achieved using the *scanf* statement as shown.

The next line demonstrates assignment of a whole structure. We assign the value of *ComponentB* to *Z*. The contents of each of the five members of *ComponentB* are copied to *Z* and so *Z* becomes a complete image of *ComponentB*. Notice that you can only perform this with structures of the same type (i.e. they are both of type *StockItem* in this case, so it is permissible). The final line will print the message:

```
We have 31 of 1n4001 DIODE in stock.
```

13.7 Self-assessment test − Structures

Consider a program in which we define the following two types of structures:

```
struct AmericanState
{
  float Size;
  long int Population;
};

struct AsianCountry
{
  float Size;
  long int Population;
  char Capitol[10];
};
```

We then define the following variables:

```
struct AmericanState  A,Kansas={2.2e5,3000000};
struct AsianCountry B,Nepal={4.5e6,5000000,
                             "Kathmandu"};
```

Which of the following assignments are legal and, of those that are legal, what value is passed to where?

a)   B=Kansas;
b)   A.Size=Kansas;
c)   B.Population=Nepal.Population;
d)   B.Population=A.Population;
e)   A=Kansas;
f)   B.Capitol=Nepal.Capitol;

Answers:

a) This is illegal and will cause a compilation error. The variable on the left-hand side is of type *AsianCountry* while the variable referred to on the right-hand side is of type *AmericanState*. The compiler will only allow assignment of structures if they are of the same type.   b) Again this is illegal. The left-hand variable is of type *long int* and the right-hand side is of type *AmericanState*.
c) Both variables are of type *long int* and so this is legal. The result is the value of 5000000 being placed in *B.Population*.   d) This is legal since both variables are of type *long int*, even though the types of the parent structures *A* and *B* are different. However, the actual value placed into *B.Population* is unknown, since *A* was not initialised.   e) This is legal since both variables are of the same type. The result is that all the data in all members of variable *Kansas* is copied into variable *A*.   f) This in principle is legal since both variables are strings. However, a compilation error will occur here for another reason. Recall that with strings one string cannot be directly assigned to another string. Instead, we would need to use the *strcpy* function:

```
strcpy(B.Capitol,Nepal.Capitol);
```

13.8   Arrays of structures

When using structures, we usually find that we need to hold many data 'records' in memory for processing. In the example for the stock control program we might have thousands of records, one for each type of component. It would be very awkward and laborious to program if we had to define a separate variable for each component. Instead, we can create an array of structures. We are already familiar with arrays of simple data types, such as the result of this definition:

```
int  MyArray[5];
```

This results in the following variables being created in memory:

MyArray

This array has five 'boxes' numbered 0..4, each of which is of type *int* (i.e. can hold a single integer value). It is possible to create an array where each 'box' in the array is a structure rather than a single variable as above. Consider this example, in which we hold details of the planets in the solar system in the following structure:

```
struct PlanetRecord
{
  char    Name[10];
  float   OrbitDist;
  float   Diameter;
};
```

This structure holds the planet name as a string, the orbital distance from the sun and the planet's diameter (N.B. we have used *floats* for the last two values which can be very large). We define an array to hold the data for all nine planets as:

```
struct PlanetRecord SolarSyst[9];
```

However, this array will be uninitialised. We can initialise the array at the same time as defining it as follows, in an order which represents the order of the planets from the sun outwards:

```
struct PlanetRecord SolarSyst[9]=
{
  {"Mercury", 35.9e6,  3000},
  {"Venus",   67.1e6,  7480},
  {"Earth",   92.8e6,  7926},
  {"Mars",    141e6,   4999},
  {"Jupiter", 483e6,   88439},
  {"Saturn",  886e6,   75000},
  {"Uranus",  178e7,   30875},
  {"Neptune", 279e7,   37200},
  {"Pluto",   300e7,   2000},
};
```

The resulting variable called *SolarSyst* has the following structure in memory:

Name	OrbitDist	Diameter	
"Mercury"	35.9e6	3000	0
"Venus"	67.1e6	7480	1
"Earth"	92.8e6	7926	2
"Mars"	141e6	4999	3
"Jupiter"	483e6	88439	4
"Saturn"	886e6	75000	5
"Uranus"	178e7	30875	6
"Neptune"	279e7	37200	7
"Pluto"	300e7	2000	8

Each element of the array *SolarSyst* is a structure of type *PlanetRecord*, which in turn consists of three members. To access any particular structure member, we specify the array name followed by an array index in square braces, followed by a dot and the structure member tag that we require. For example, the following reference yields the distance of the third planet (number 2 in the array) from the sun (93 million miles):

```
SolarSyst[2].OrbitDist
```

Another example might be to print out the name of the last planet. This could be done with the following statement:

```
printf("The last planet is %s",SolarSyst[8].Name);
```

This results in the message:

```
The last planet is Pluto
```

Because we have all our information properly structured, it is now easy to perform a variety of tasks. For instance, to print the order of planets from the sun we can simply write:

```
for (n=0;n<=8;n++)
{
  printf("%s \n",SolarSyst[n].Name);
}
```

where *n* is an *int* variable. The result is this list on the screen:

```
Mercury
Venus
  .
  .
  .
Pluto
```

Another task that we may want to perform is to calculate the distances between the orbits of any two user-specified planets. The following section of code achieves this:

```
printf("Enter position from sun of two planets.");
scanf("%i",&Plnt1);
scanf("%i",&Plnt2);

dist=SolarSyst[Plnt1].OrbitDist-
            SolarSyst[Plnt2].OrbitDist;
printf("Distance from %s to %s is %e.",
    SolarSyst[Plnt1].Name, SolarSyst[Plnt2].name,
    dist);
```

where *Plnt1* and *Plnt2* are of type *int* and *dist* is a *float*. The result, if the user enters 4 and 2, would be

```
Distance from Mars to Venus is 74e6.
```

Notice one small problem with this program. Depending on the order in which we enter the two planets, we may get the distance as a negative number.

13.9   Passing records to functions

We are already familiar with how we can pass values to functions as parameters. Previously, we have only concentrated on passing simple variable types. However, by exactly the same mechanism we can pass a structure as a parameter. Still using the example of the planets program, let us assume that we want a function to print all the information about any particular planet we pass to it (note that *printf* cannot print whole records, it can only print it as a sequence of its members). The function might appear as follows:

```
void  PrintPlanet( struct PlanetRecord P )
{
  printf("Planet Name          %s \n",P.Name);
  printf("Distance from sun    %f \n",P.OrbitDist);
  printf("Diameter             %f \n",P.Diameter);
}
```

When called, this procedure is passed a single structure of type *PlanetRecord*. The contents of this record is copied into the local variable *P* and each member of the structure *P* is then printed. There is no return value. A typical call of this function might take the form:

```
PrintPlanet( SolarSyst[2] );
```

This results in the contents of element 2 of the array *SolarSyst*, which is a single structure of type *PlanetRecord* being copied to variable *P* in the function *PrintPlanet* when it is called. The resulting output is therefore:

```
Planet Name         Earth
Distance from sun 9.6e6
Diameter            8000
```

Notice that in the definition of *PrintPlanet* there is a reference to the structure type *PlanetRecord*. The declaration of *PlanetRecord* must be done such that it is visible to the *PrintPlanet* function, so its declaration should be done globally (i.e. outside of all functions). However, it does not matter if the array *SolarSyst* is global or local and unseen by *PrintPlanet*, since *PrintPlanet* makes no reference to it.

As final note, here it is more usual to pass the address of a structure variable to a function, rather than a copy of the structure itself. This results in using less memory and faster code. This means that we pass the address of a structure to the function. The function parameter must then be defined to a pointer to the structure type being received, so that subsequent references in the function access the structure via this pointer. The call to print planet then takes the form:

```
PrintPlanet (&SolarSyst[2]);
```

The function definition is then as follows:

```
void  PrintPlanet( struct PlanetRecord *P )
{
  printf("Planet Name         %s \n",*P.Name);
  printf("Distance from sun  %f \n",*P.OrbitDist);
  printf("Diameter           %f \n",*P.Diameter);
}
```

13.10 Returning structures from functions

As we have already seen, we can write functions which produce return values. Previously, we have written functions which return values of simple type (e.g. *int, float, char*). Logically, we should be able to write functions which return a structure type variable. However, although there is nothing wrong with this idea in concept, most versions of C compilers do not allow this. The only return type which functions can have are the standard simple types. The reason for this is to keep the compiler simpler and the compiled code simpler and faster. To get around this problem, we can return a pointer to a structure variable as a means of returning structure results from functions.

This completes our introduction to structures. We have covered enough ground to allow you to perform most tasks you could require. There now follows a simple case study using structures.

13.11 Case study — Telephone directory

It is required to build a simple phone directory system for use by receptionists in a small company (in this case only 15 employees, but it could potentially be thousands). Our first consideration is, how do we hold all the data required about each person, such as their extension number, surname and initial? Clearly, this is a case for using structures. We declare a structure type as follows:

```
struct Employee
{
  char Name[10];
  char Initial;
  int  Extension;
};
```

This forms the template for the basic storage unit (a record) for the details of each person and it is given the name *Employee*. Notice that this is a declaration and no variables have been created yet; we have simply defined a new type. We now need to create an array of these records to store all the information required. The array is defined as a local variable of the *main* function, as follows:

```
#define MaxEmployees 20

struct Employee StaffDirectory[MaxEmployees];
```

We have created an array called *StaffDirectory* which consists of up to twenty records (note that *MaxEmployees* is defined as 20 earlier). The next step is to initialise the array to hold all the information of the directory. This is done using a function called *SetUpDirectory*, to which we pass the directory array (N.B. remember that when passing arrays just the memory address of the array is passed). We could write the function *SetUpDirectory* such that it loads each name and extension number into the array directly, with all the information being written in the source code file. However, this is not very flexible, as it means that any changes require editing the program and recompiling it. A better way is to read the information into the array from a file of text. This file can easily be edited when any changes occur, without the need to change the source code. The format of this file, which is called *direct.dat* and is in the directory *public,* is as follows:

```
\public\direct.dat
```

A	Bury	342
B	Sanders	123
R	White	125
S	Charlton	232
T	Sanders	343
P	Smith	342
H	Doe	112
J	Houston	332
A	Jackson	565
C	Thomas	542
D	Bury	453
B	Terry	123
P	Elsdon	121
A	Jerram	221
D	Groom	454 [EOF]

Notice that each record is terminated by a \n character to indicate that a new line begins. When loaded into the array, the result is a data structure as shown below:

```
StaffDirectory
```

Name	Initial	Extension	
"Bury"	'A'	342	0
"Sanders"	'B'	123	1
.	.	.	.
.	.	.	.
"Jerram"	'A'	221	13
"Groom"	'D'	454	14

We will not describe in detail the operation of the function *SetUpDirectory*, since it is not important to illustrating the use of structures. However, readers should be able to follow the workings of this function if they have understood the chapter on file handling. Notice that the function *SetUpDirectory* will return an integer, which tells the rest of the program how many records were read. This value is stored in the variable *size* in the *main* function. If any errors are found in the format of the input file, then the program terminates with a suitable message. Remember that on IBM machines the file pathnames use backslash characters (\) which in C is the start of an escape sequence. Therefore, to quote a backslash in a file pathname we must use the escape sequence for it which is two backslashes (\\).

From this point on the program is fairly straightforward. The program reads a string from the user, which represents the surname of the person for whom they need an extension number, it then looks up this string in the list of names and, if found, the record containing the name is printed.

The *main* function contains a never-ending loop (using *while(1)* which always continues looping), in which we first read a string containing a person's name.

Then a call to the function *FindAndPrint* is made and it is passed the string as an argument to the parameter array called *Str*, a reference to the data array, and also the number of records in the array.

```
void FindAndPrint(char Str[10], struct Employee
                dir[], int size)
{
  int N=0;
  int MatchFound=0;

  do
  {
    if (strcmp(Str,dir[N].Name)==0)
    {
      PrintRecord(dir[N]);
      MatchFound=1;
    }
    N++;
  }
  while (N<size);

  /*Test if name was found.Print message if not*/
  if (MatchFound==0) printf("Name not found");
}
```

This function examines the array from the top of the data to the bottom and for each record, compares the *Name* member field with the string containing the user supplied name contained in *Str*. To do this we use the string comparison function *strcmp*, which returns a zero if they match (note that this is case sensitive, which may cause problems − an improvement might be to convert all names to upper case as they are read, which is simple to achieve). If no match is made in the loop, then an appropriate message is printed. Each time a match is made we call the function *PrintRecord* to which we pass the record to be printed. This function is defined as follows:

```
void PrintRecord(struct Employee Rec)
{
  printf("%c. %s is on ext. %i", Rec.Initial,
    Rec.Name,Rec.Extension);
}
```

The record is copied to the local variable in *PrintRecord* called *Rec* and then the values of the members are printed.

The complete program is as follows:

```
/*Phone directory system for small organisation*/
/*Allows search for a number given a name      */
```

```
#include <stdio.h>
#include <string.h>
#include <stdlib.h>

#define MaxEmployees 50   /*Max size of directory*/

/* Declare structure for one employee globally */

struct  Employee
{
  char    Name[10];
  char    Initial;
  int     Extension;
};

/* Function prototypes */
void PrintRecord(struct Employee Rec);
void FindAndPrint(char Str[10], struct Employee
            dir[], int size);
int SetUpDirectory(struct Employee dir[]);

/**************************************************/
main()
{
  struct  Employee StaffDirectory[MaxEmployees];
  char Name[10];
  int size;

  size=SetUpDirectory(StaffDirectory);
  while (1)
  {
    printf("\nEnter surname:-");
    scanf("%s",Name);
    FindAndPrint(Name, StaffDirectory, size);
  }
}

/**************************************************/
/* Set up directory. Initialises the array       */
/* which is passed as parameter `dir`             */

int SetUpDirectory(struct Employee dir[])
{
  FILE *dirfile;      /* File pointer */
  int status, N;      /* scanf return */
  int N               /* Records read into array*/

  /* Open file containing directory */
  dirfile=fopen("\\public\\direct.dat","r");

  /*Test if file opened ok.If not, terminate */
  if (dirfile==NULL)
```

```
{
  printf("\n\nError. Cannot open file\a");
  exit(0);
}

/*Read records until array full or EOF reached*/
/* N counts records so far read */

N=0;
do
{
  /* Read Initial. A single character */
  status=fscanf(dirfile,"%c",&dir[N].Initial);

  /* If status<>1 error in file or EOF hit */
  if (status!=1)
  {
    printf("\nError in file at line %i",N);
    exit(0);
  }

  /*Read surname.A string up to 10 characters*/
  status=fscanf(dirfile,"%10s",dir[N].Name);

  /* If status<>1 error in file or EOF hit */
  if (status!=1)
  {
    printf("\nError in file at line %i",N);
    exit(0);
  }

  /* Read extension number */
  status=fscanf(dirfile,"%i",
      &dir[N].Extension);

  /* If status<>0 error in file or EOF hit */

  if (status!=1)
  {
    printf("\nError in file at line %i",N);
    exit(0);
  }

  /* Increment records read. Also read file  */
  /* to beginning of next line               */
  N++;
  status=fscanf(dirfile,"\n");

  /* Loop unless array full or EOF hit */
}
while (status!=EOF && N<MaxEmployees);
return N;
```

```
}
/**********************************************/
/* Prints the employees record passed into    */
/* variable Rec                                */

void PrintRecord(struct Employee Rec)
{
  printf("%c. %s is on extension
    %i\n",Rec.Initial,Rec.Name,Rec.Extension);
}

/**********************************************/

void  FindAndPrint (char  Str[10],
        struct Employee dir[] , int size)
{
  int N=0;
  int MatchFound=0;

  do
  {
    if (strcmp(Str,dir[N].Name)==0)
    {
      PrintRecord(dir[N]);
      MatchFound=1;
    }
    N++;
  }
  while (N<size);

  /* Test if name was found. Print message if not */
  if (MatchFound==0) printf("Name not found");
}
```

13.12 Summary

- The user can declare new types of data item called structures, which can consist of a collection of members of simple types.

- Once a structure type has been declared, this can be used to define a structure variable. Note that the word *struct* appears in front of the type identifier in variable definitions.

- Structures can be assigned as whole entities or, alternatively, each component member can be manipulated independently using the member tag identifier.

- Structured variables can be passed to functions as arguments, in the same manner as any other single variable.

- Structures cannot be used as return types from functions. A way around this is to return a pointer to an existing structure variable, into which the results of the function are placed.

- Arrays can be defined using structure types. Storage of large amounts of structured data is then possible.

13.13 Programming exercises

1) A complex number could be represented as a structure declared as follows:

```
struct complex
  {
    double Real;
    double Imag;
  };
```

Write a program which uses this structure and performs the following tasks using an appropriately defined function for each task.

a) Reads in two complex numbers (you will need to use global variables for this unless you are familiar with the use of pointers).

b) Adds the two numbers to produce a third (again, globals need to be used unless the reader is familiar with the use of pointers).

c) Calculates and displays the modulus of each of the three complex numbers (use a function which accepts a structure as an argument and returns a double).

d) Calculates and displays the argument (in degrees) of each of the three numbers.

2) A simple circuit simulator is to be used to investigate the circuit of Figure 13.1. A description of the circuit (a netlist) may appear as follows:

```
VSOURCE   0    4    2V
RINPUT         4    2    1K
L1             2    0    0.1H
C1             2    0    0.00001F
RBIAS          2    10   10K
```

```
DCLAMP          7   0   1N4001
IBIAS          10   7   0.01A
```

Each line consists of a component name, two node numbers between which it is connected, and a string representing the value or component type. Write a program to read this information from file and perform on it some checks. These are:

a) That there is at least one connection to earth. The earth node is always labelled as node 0.

b) That all other nodes have at least two connections. In the process of doing this, print out the number of connections to each node. Note that node names are integer numbers, but do not necessarily run from 0 upwards continuously.

c) That all component names are valid. A component name consists of an initial letter to indicate the type of component (e.g. 'R' for resistor) and then a string of any characters (up to ten). The components that it supports are resistors(R), capacitors(C), inductors(L), voltage sources(V), current sources(I) and diodes(D). The case of the input file should be unimportant.

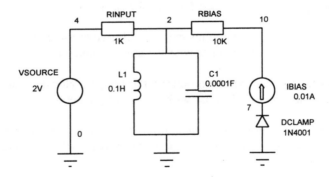

Figure 13.1 Simulator circuit

To write this program, first set up a suitable data structure to hold the information into which the information is initially read from a file. Then functions for subsequent processing can be added. Produce several netlists to test the function of the program.

14 Low-level Operations

14.1 Introduction

In many engineering applications it is necessary to be able to interact with external devices. In particular, control applications require the computer to control motors, valves, lights, etc. and read in information from switches, temperature sensors and various other transducers. This requires two new techniques to be explored. Firstly, we must look at how data can be written to, or read from, remote devices. Secondly, we must look at techniques for manipulating the data required by these external devices, which is often represented in the form of individual bits.

14.2 Input and output ports

There is no standard defined for C for low-level input and output operations to peripheral devices. However, most compilers offer functions, such as *in* and *out*, which we shall describe in general terms in the following section. To understand their operation, we must first look at the hardware required to control communication with peripherals.

Communication by the CPU with the outside world takes place through hardware devices called interfaces, which provide the programmer with logical communication channels called ports. Interfaces are usually single chips and come in either serial or parallel varieties. A parallel port allows the CPU to communicate along a parallel bus of wires. A typical parallel port would have eight wires coming from it for connection with peripheral devices, allowing the CPU to write or read a byte in one operation. A serial port will only have one data line coming from it. Therefore, for the CPU to write or read a byte, the data must be transmitted to or from the peripheral device as a series of pulses (time multiplexed). This makes the transmission process more complex and slower, but is preferable for long distance communication, where it would be expensive to have eight or more wires.

We will limit our discussion to parallel ports, in order to illustrate the C functions used, but it should be remembered that serial ports are important devices and their use is widespread.

14.3 Controlling ports

A computer may have dozens of ports for different purposes and so it is necessary to distinguish between them. Therefore, each port device will have one or more addresses associated with it. We can then write programs which instruct the CPU to interact with particular ports for which we specify the addresses. A typical interface device is the 8255 chip, for which a schematic is shown in Figure 14.1.

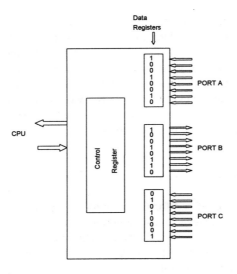

Figure 14.1 8255 Interface chip

One feature of this chip is that it actually implements three ports (A, B and C). Also, each port is reconfigurable, such that it may act as an input or an output port. We have shown ports A and C to be configured as input ports and B as an output port. The configuration of the port is determined by the contents of the control register, containing a byte of data which the CPU must initially set to achieve the desired port operation. Each port has an associated data register and, for an input port, this register will contain the state of the eight input wires. If the CPU needs to read from this port then it will read the contents of this register. For output ports, the data register contains the state of the output wires that it is driving. Therefore, if the CPU wants to change the output, it changes the contents of this register.

The addresses of the ports are determined by the way the chip is wired to the computer's data and address buses. We will assume that this chip has four associated addresses, as follows:

0x300   Port A data register
0x301   Port B data register
0x302   Port C data register
0x303   Control register

Notice that the control register is treated as a port data register, but by writing data to it we change the configuration of the ports, rather than writing the data out to a peripheral device. The data written to the control register is dependent on the required configuration for the application. We will not discuss the details of this here, but reference to the data sheet for the chip will reveal the possible configurations along with the control values.

14.4   *in* and *out* functions

To communicate with the port from a C program we use *in* and *out* functions. Note that these are not standard and their names and nature will change between implementations.

To use the *out* function we simply make the following call:

```
out(address,data);
```

where *data* is a byte expression and *address* is the address of an output port, e.g.:

```
out(0x301,0x55);
```

To read a byte from an input port we use the *in* function which returns a byte:

```
in(address);
```

A typical call may be as follows:

```
n=in(0x302);
```

Note that it is often possible to read and write 16-bit words. In this case there may be two varieties of I/O functions, such as *inb* and *outb* for bytes, and *inw* and *outw* for words.

A simple example which uses these functions is shown in Figure 14.2, where we have a bank of eight LEDs connected to an output port (port B) via appropriate buffering, and eight switches on an input port (port A) to switch the voltage levels between 0 and 5 V. We want to light up all the LEDs when switch 4 is in the 1 position (i.e. byte value of 16 or 0x01) and turn them off when it is in the 0 position.

We will assume that the correct value for the control register is 0x83 to configure the port. The program required will loop continuously and on each cycle will read the switches. It will then write either 0x0, or 0xFF, to the LEDs, turning them all off or all on. The program will appear as follows:

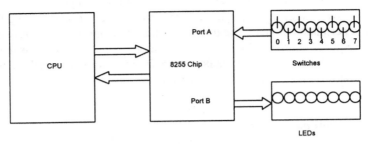

Figure 14.2 Lights and switches system

```
main()
{
    /* define byte sized variable */
    unsigned char m;

    out(0x303,0x83); /* First set up ports */

    /* Loop indefinitely */
    while (1)
    {
      m=in(0x300); /* Read switches */

      /* Turn LEDs on or off */
      if (m==0x10)
      {
        out(0xFF,0x301);/*switch 4 on,turn on LEDs*/
      }
      else
      {
        out(0x0,0x301); /* turn off LEDs */
      }
    }
}
```

This program should work under certain conditions, but notice one problem. We have assumed that all switches will be at 0, except switch four which can be 1 or 0. If any switch other than number four is at 1 then the program will not work, because the value read when switch four is at 1 will no longer be 0x10. It would be better if we could examine only the bit that corresponds to switch four, rather than the whole byte as is the case in this program. This leads us on to low-level operations.

14.5   The low-level operators

The C language has several low-level operators for the manipulation of bits, which work in a similar fashion to AND, OR, NOT and XOR logic gates and shift registers. All these operators are termed 'bitwise operators', as they deal bit by bit with the operand. The operators available are:

&	AND
|	OR
~	NOT
^	XOR
>>	Shift left
<<	Shift right

These operators are used on integer type expressions (including *char* types) and are applied to each bit position of the operands. For example, consider the following section of code:

```
unsigned char a,b,c;

a=0xAA;
b=0x0F;
c=a&c;
```

The 8-bit variables *a* and *b* will have bit patterns as follows:

a

1	0	1	0	1	0	1	0

b

0	0	0	0	1	1	1	1

If we now apply a bitwise AND operation to the right-most bits of each operand we get the result of 0 AND 1 which gives 0. The corresponding bit in variable *c* is therefore set to 0. Working to the left, the same operation is applied to the next column, giving 1 AND 1, which results in the corresponding bit in *c* being set to 1. The final result in *c* will be:

c

0	0	0	0	1	0	1	0

In practice, the CPU performs all eight AND operations in parallel to save time. The operation can be performed on any two integer type expressions, provided that they are both of the same bit-length. The lengths of such expressions may vary from 8 to 32 bits.

All the other bitwise operators operate in a similar manner, except the shift operations which are significantly different. Each operator is now described.

14.6   The NOT operator

The NOT operator has the symbol ~ and inverts each bit of the data item to which it is applied. This operation is also known as a one's complement. The truth table for this is simply:

Input	Output
0	1
1	0

Note that this is a unary operator and is often used to invert the output from one of the other bitwise operators to form NAND, NOR and XNOR functions. The following example shows how to use the operator.

```
int pattern, result;
pattern= 0x1F;        /* 0000 0000 0001 1111 */
result= ~pattern;     /* 1111 1111 1110 0000 */
```

14.7   The AND operator

This operator uses the symbol & and provides the AND operation for each bit between two operands. The truth table is shown below:

A	B	Result
0	0	0
0	1	0
1	0	0
1	1	1

A typical application of this operator is to test the state of an individual bit (as required in the light-and-switches example earlier). We can effectively 'mask' out all the bit positions that we are not interested in by ANDing them with 0. The result will therefore always have 0 in these positions since anything ANDed with 0 gives 0. For the bit position that we are interested in we AND it with 1. Therefore, the state of this bit is effectively copied to the result. To illustrate this, consider the light and switches example in which we read the state of the switches into a variable *m*. We now need to test the state of the bit in position 4 of the variable *m*, for which we use the following code:

```
unsigned char n,m,mask;
mask=0x10;
```

```
        .
        .
m=in(0x302);
n=m&mask;
if (m==0)
  {
        .
        .
```

The variable *mask* is set such that all its bits, except that the one in position 4 are equal to 0. Now, assume that we read the switches and *m* is set to 01010010. If we now AND these, we get the following:

m

0	1	0	1	0	0	1	0

mask

0	0	0	1	0	0	0	0

n

0	0	0	1	0	0	0	0

The result in *n* is not the integer value zero, indicating that the bit in position four of *m* is set (i.e. the switch is on). Alternatively, the value in *m* might be 10101110, in which case we have the following:

m

1	0	1	0	1	1	1	0

mask

0	0	0	1	0	0	0	0

n

0	0	0	0	0	0	0	0

In this case the result in *n* is the integer value zero, indicating that the switch is off. We have effectively ignored all the other switches and the program is now only sensitive to the state of one switch, as determined by the mask.

14.8 The OR operator

The OR operator uses the symbol | and its truth table is shown below.

A	B	Result
0	0	0
0	1	1
1	0	1
1	1	1

This operator would be used to merge two bit patterns together. This can be useful in constructing masks when it is necessary to look at a number of different bits. For example, to construct a mask to mask out all bits except bits 1, 2 and 5 we could write the following:

```
int mask,mask1,mask2,mask3,mask5;

mask0=0x0001;            /*0000 0000 0000 0001*/
mask1=0x0002;            /*0000 0000 0000 0010*/
mask2=0x0004;            /*0000 0000 0000 0100*/
mask5=0x0010;            /*0000 0000 0010 0000*/
mask=mask5 | mask2 | mask1;  /*0000 0000 0010 0110*/
```

14.9   The XOR operator

This operator uses the ^ symbol and performs a logical exclusive-or function, for which the truth table is shown below. It is used in the same manner as the AND and OR operators.

A	B	Result
0	0	0
0	1	1
1	0	1
1	1	0

This operator is useful for toggling a selected bit, by exclusive OR-ing it with '1'.

14.10   The shift operators

Shift operators are unary operators and they move the whole bit pattern of the operand either left or right by a specified number of places. For example, a shift left of one position has the following effect:

Original value

1	0	1	1	1	1	0	1

Shifted value

0	1	1	1	1	0	1	0

Note that the value of the left-most bit is lost and a 0 is inserted on the right. Similarly, a shift right operation by two places has the following effect:

Original value	0	0	0	1	0	0	0	0

Shifted value	0	0	0	0	0	1	0	0

These operations use the $<<$ or $>>$ symbols, followed by an integer expression to indicate the number of places to shift. For example:

```
unsigned char a, b;

a = 0x0F;        /* 0000 1111 */
b = a << 2;      /* 0011 1100 */
printf("%x shifted twice left gives %x", a, b);
```

The resulting message is:

```
0F shifted twice left gives 3C
```

A point worth noting is that if an integer is shifted one place right, its value is halved and if shifted left one place its value is doubled.

There is one other important point to note concerning right shifting. If a byte is used to store a negative value in two's complement (i.e. it is defined as a signed int or signed char) the right shifting it will not halve the value. For example:

```
11111100    = -4 in decimal
01111110    = +126 in decimal after one right shift
```

This is because a '0' has been introduced from the left, changing the sign to positive. Instead, a '1' is introduced to preserve the sign:

```
11111100    = -4 in decimal
11111110    = -2 in decimal after one shift
```

In this case the insertion from the left of a '1' gives us the expected answer of -2. Therefore, when performing a right shift, the value of the bit inserted from the left is the same as the left-most bit before the shift (i.e. if the left-most bit is '1', then a '1' is inserted after the shift, or if the left-most bit is '0', then a 0 is inserted). This preserves the sign of the data and we obtain the expected halving of the original value.

14.11 Case study – Temperature monitor

A system is required to monitor the minimum and maximum temperature of an oven from the time the program is run. One solution uses a thermistor to convert the temperature to an analogue voltage and then an analogue-to-digital convertor to convert this voltage to an eight-bit value. The hardware system is shown in Figure 14.3.

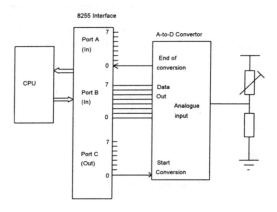

Figure 14.3 Temperature monitor

Notice the signal connections to the A-to-D convertor. The eight-bit output of the convertor is connected to port B of the interface chip, requiring that this port is configured for input. The *start conversion* signal causes the A-to-D convertor to perform a conversion operation when a rising edge is detected on this input. Therefore, one line of port C is used to drive this signal. The conversion takes a certain amount of time and so the A-to-D convertor has an output called *end of conversion* which is low when the conversion cycle is in progress and high after the cycle has finished, meaning that the result is present on the data lines. We use a single line of port A to read this signal. The complete program is as follows:

```
#include <stdio.h>
#include <conio.h> /* For in and out functions */
#define PORTA    0x300  /* Port Addresses */
#define PORTB    0x301
#define PORTC    0x302
#define CONTROL  0x303

int ReadTemp(void);      /* Function prototype */

/*********************************************/
main()
{
  int mintemp,maxtemp,temp;
```

```
out(CONTROL,0x7F);      /* Configure ports */

/* Dummy read to ensure A-to-D initialised */
ReadTemp();

/* Get starting temp */
temp=ReadTemp();
printf("Starting temp=%i",temp);
mintemp=temp;
maxtemp=temp;

while(1)
{
  temp=ReadTemp();
  if (temp<mintemp)
  {
    mintemp=temp;
    printf("New lowest temp=%i",mintemp);
  }
  if (temp>maxtemp)
  {
    maxtemp=temp;
    printf("New highest temp=%i",maxtemp);
  }
}
}
/*************************************************/
/*This function starts A-to-D conversion, waits  */
/* until completed and then reads result. This   */
/* is then converted to temperature in degrees C */

int ReadTemp(void)
{
  unsigned char AtoD,Finished;
  int t;

  /* Toggle Start conversion signal */
  out(PORTC,0x00);
  out(PORTC,0x01);

  /* Wait for End of conversion*/
  do
  {
    Finished=in(PORTA);     /* Read port */
    /* Mask appropriate bits */
    Finished=Finished & 0x01;
  }
  while (Finished==0);

  /* Conversion finished. Read result */
  AtoD=in(PORTB);
```

```
/* Convert to degrees celsius and return */
t=AtoD*12.6+120;
return t;
}
```

Note that the value read from the A-to-D does not represent temperature exactly. We will assume that a unit of the A-to-D output represents 12.6° C and there is an offset of 120° C. Note that because we have a *float* type constant value in the expression, the whole expression is evaluated using floating point arithmetic. However, a truncation occurs on the final result, due to the assignment to an integer.

14.12 Summary

● Most compilers supply non-standard functions to allow input and output of data to ports.

● Interfaces are hardware devices which allow the CPU to communicate to external equipment through logical channels called ports. There are many different interface devices available and many are reconfigurable to maximise their flexibility.

● Low-level operators allow manipulation of the individual bits of a data item.

15 Graphics

15.1 Introduction

This chapter examines the basic principles of computer graphics and looks at how to perform some simple graphical operations on a personal computer type system. These will cover the use of coordinate systems, library functions and some useful techniques to make the job of programming graphical applications easier. It should be noted throughout that although most PC type machines have compilers which offer graphical capabilities, the functions supplied are all non-standard and there will be great variance between implementations.

15.2 Display hardware

In most modern machines the monitor is driven by a graphics adapter. This is essentially a small processor in its own right, which produces video signals from a memory image of the display. The adapter will have its own memory in which to store the displayed image. This means that there is little overhead on the main CPU in terms of driving the display and no use of main memory.

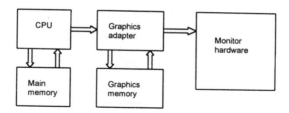

Figure 15.1 Display hardware

It is often the case that the graphics adapter can operate in different modes and offer a selection of different resolutions and numbers of colours. It may also be that the machine has a specific mode for text display and other modes for graphics. For example, an IBM type machine may have an adapter with a text screen mode designed for the simple display of text, as well as a selection of graphics modes. Most commonly, the graphics mode is of the VGA type format (Video Graphics Adapter) which allows good resolution and a useful number of colours.

A C compiler will probably be supplied with a graphics library (which is non-standard). If necessary, this will provide a function to set the mode of the graphics adapter. For example:

```
setvideomode (VGA);
```

which could be used to set the adapter to VGA mode, or

```
setvideomode (DEFAULT);
```

to set adapter to a default mode (usually text mode). Note that the names, format and usage of such a function will differ between implementations, so the compiler documentation will need to be consulted. The values of the arguments above (VGA, DEFAULT) are defined in the graphics library header file and this is a common way to identify adapter modes. Again, the names used may differ widely.

15.3   Physical coordinates

When the adapter is in its selected mode, we need to be able to identify points on the screen at which to draw an item or display text. This is done using a simple X,Y coordinate system. When using adapters with text mode, the coordinate system is usually organised as shown in Figure 15.2.

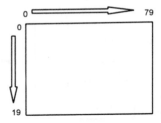

Figure 15.2 Text screen coordinates

A typical size would be 20 rows by 80 columns, but this varies, and many adapters have a selection of text modes with different resolutions. A common operation is to place the text cursor (i.e. position at which text will next appear) at a point on the screen, using a library function such as:

```
settextposition (row_coord, column_coord);
```

For example:

```
settextposition (10,38);
printf ("Hello");
```

would print the word 'Hello' in the centre of the screen shown in Figure 15.2. Again it must be emphasised that the names and usage of such a function will vary between compilers.

When using a graphics type display (such as VGA mode on an IBM PC type machine) the screen coordinate system is mode likely to be similar to that in Figure 15.3.

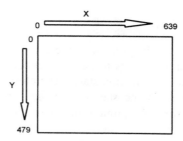

Figure 15.3 Graphical display coordinates

The most basic operation usually available for use on a graphics display is a plotting function. This allows a single dot or picture element (commonly called a pixel) to be set to a certain colour. This usually has the form:

```
plot(x_coord,y_coord);
```

although other function names such as *setpixel* are common. This sets the pixel with the given X-Y coordinates to the present drawing colour. The drawing colour is usually set using another function such as *setcolor*, which accepts a colour index that is usually an integer value representing one of the available colours. As an example, the following code draws a red dot (assuming that 5 is the colour index for red) at the position 40 along and 400 down on the screen of Figure 15.3:

```
setcolor(5);
plot(40,400);
```

The values of colour indexes can usually be found in the compiler documentation, or there may be defined identifiers for colours in the graphics library header file.

Throughout the rest of this chapter we will assume a screen coordinate system as just described.

15.4   Graphics library functions

The number and nature of the graphical library functions will vary, but we will cover here some of the more common and simple functions which can be used to create more complex functions as required. A basic requirement is to be able to draw straight lines. Therefore, there will be available a function such as:

```
line(x1,y1,x2,y2);
```

which draws a line between the point with the coordinates *x1,y1* and the point *x2,y2*. A slight variation on this is to have the concept of a current position, from which the next drawing function starts. Therefore, it may be necessary to move the current position to the start of the line, using a function such as *moveto*, and then draw from this point a line to another point, using a function such as *lineto*. For example:

```
moveto(100,150);
lineto(120,170);
```

draws a line from 100,150 to 120,170. Note that the coordinates are usually *int* type expressions. Another common function is for drawing circles. A simple case would be a form as follows:

```
circle(x,y,r);
```

which draws a circle at centre *x,y* with radius *r*. A variation on this is an ellipse function which is used for circles and other ellipses. To describe an ellipse, a common method is to specify a rectangle into which the ellipse must fit (N.B. a square will produce a circle). This only requires the two coordinates of opposite corners to be specified (see Figure 15.4).

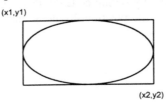

Figure 15.4 Specifying an ellipse

A typical ellipse function would therefore be called as follows:

```
ellipse(x1,y1,x2,y2);
```

Other drawing functions will also be available. For example, there may be a rectangle function or triangle function, but these are simple to create ourselves, using the line drawing function. Another commonly available function, which is often worth investigation, is one to draw circular arcs.

All the drawing functions so far listed draw in outline, using the present drawing colour (determined by the last call of a function such as *setcolor*). It is often desirable to fill in the shapes that we have drawn to create solid areas. Therefore, a function such as *fillarea* is often available. This allows an area bounded by a certain colour to be filled with the same or a different colour. A typical call is as follows:

```
fillarea(x,y,boundary_colour);
```

where *x,y* is a point inside the area to be filled and *boundary_colour* is the colour index of the boundary of the area. The colour used to fill the area is the current drawing colour. Therefore to draw a red circle (colour index 5) with a green interior (colour index 7) of radius 100, centred on 200,300, we would write the following:

```
setcolor(5);
circle(200,300);
setcolor(7);
fillarea(200,300,5);
```

Care must be taken to ensure that the boundary has no gaps, or else the fill colour spills out of the area and can potentially fill the whole screen as shown in Figure 15.5 where a red box is being filled with green.

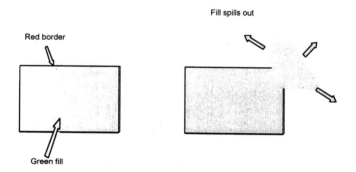

Figure 15.5 Filling areas

Most graphics libraries will allow text to be displayed graphically, using a function such as:

```
outtext(x,y,text_string);
```

which displays the text at the pixel position X-Y. However, this is usually more complicated than suggested here, as the text font (i.e. the pattern of dots for each character) often needs to be loaded in memory as the program runs. Also, the size of the text displayed may be variable. This is something that should be investigated from the compiler documentation.

Other functions will also exist in the graphics library for drawing and other tasks such as clearing the screen.

15.5   Coordinate mapping

For many applications it is inconvenient to have the origin of the screen coordinates at the top left corner. It is also unnatural in many cases for the Y coordinate to increase downwards rather than upwards. Consider a case in which we want to draw a graph, where the origin of the graph is in the centre of the screen. We therefore need to draw the axes and then plot the curve relative to the origin of the graph and not the origin of the screen coordinates.

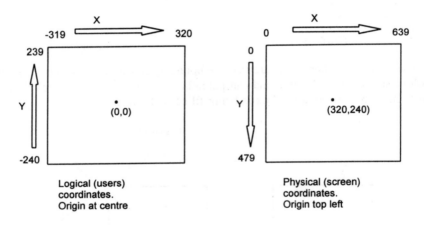

Figure 15.6 Coordinate mapping

We are going to introduce the concept of mapping, which will allow the programmer to assume that the origin of the screen coordinates is in a more natural position (e.g. the centre) and the Y coordinates increase upwards. What is required to achieve this is automatic conversion from the user's coordinate system to the physical screen coordinates each time something is drawn. For example, to plot the graph previously mentioned, we might have the coordinate systems as shown in Figure 15.6.

Therefore, if the user wanted to draw a dot at the centre of the screen then he expects the call:

```
plot(0,0);
```

to do the trick. However, as we know, the *plot* function will instead plot the point at the top left-hand corner. What is required is a new plot function, which accepts the users coordinates, converts these to physical coordinates, and then calls the original plot function. Such a function can be defined as follows:

```
void myplot(int x, int y)
{
  plot(x+320,240-y);
}
```

Therefore, using the user's coordinates the call:

```
myplot(0,0);
```

now becomes equivalent to:

```
plot(320,240);
```

which plots the point in the centre of the screen. The user can therefore happily assume that the centre of the screen is the origin, provided that he does not call the *plot* function directly, but instead uses his own function *myplot*, which maps the user logical coordinates to the physical screen coordinates. This is achieved by simply adding an offset equal to half the screen size to the user's coordinates. Note that for the Y coordinate, the user's coordinate is subtracted from half the screen width. This means that, in the user's logical coordinate system, Y now increases upwards and not downwards. By using different offsets the user's origin can be placed anywhere on the screen.

A whole series of mapped drawing functions can be produced, all of which work with the user's chosen coordinate system, such as the examples which follow:

```
#include <graph.h> /* Graphics lib. header */

/* Define user's origin on the screen in      */
/* physical screen coordinates                 */
#define CENTRE_X 320   /*  X pixel coordinate */
#define CENTRE_Y 240   /*  Y pixel coordinate */

main()
{
  . /* performs drawing task */
  .
```

```
}
/**************************************************/
/* Draw circle at x,y in user coords with      */
/* radius of r pixels                          */
void mycircle(int x,int y,int r)
{
  ellipse(x+CENTRE_X+r,  CENTRE_Y+r-y,
          x+CENTRE_X-r,  CENTRE_Y-r-y);
}

/***************************************************/
/* Fill in current colour from point x,y (in    */
/* user coordinates) to a boundary of colour    */
/* index given by c                             */
void myfill(int x,int y,int c)
{
  fillarea(x+CENTRE_X,  CENTRE_Y-y,  c);
}
/***************************************************/
/* Draw line in current colour from x1,y1 to    */
/* x2,y2 using user coordinates                 */
void myline(int x1,int y1,int x2,int y2)
{
  _moveto(x1+CENTRE_X,CENTRE_Y-y1);
  _lineto(x2+CENTRE_X,CENTRE_Y-y2);
}
```

Note that the offsets *CENTRE_X* and *CENTRE_Y* are defined as constant values. This allows the origin to be completely shifted if necessary with one easy edit.

This approach to introducing tailor-made basic graphics functions is very powerful and flexible. Such functions also make the task of programming graphical applications very much simpler. There now follows an example which uses this approach to plot graphs whose origin (so far as the user is concerned) is mid-way down the screen and close to the left-hand edge.

15.6   Case study − Fourier composition

A square wave can be considered as a sum of its sinusoidal harmonics, according to the equation:

$$F(\theta) = \sin(\theta) + \frac{1}{3}\sin(3\theta) + \frac{1}{5}\sin(5\theta) + \frac{1}{7}\sin(7\theta) + \frac{1}{9}\sin(9\theta)...$$

where θ is the angular distance along the square wave (360° per cycle). The greater the number of terms (harmonic components) included in the summation, the better final approximation will be to a square wave.

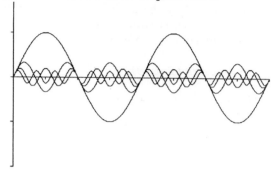

Figure 15.7 Fundamental and odd harmonics

The program is written using the graphics library from Microsoft QuickC, but similar functions will be available in other compilers. The program starts with a number of definitions of constant values. These include the programmer's coordinate system origin, which is at 100,240 in physical coordinates, the lengths in pixels of the X and Y axes, and the maximum values which the X and Y axes represent (i.e. the X axis represents 0° to 720° and the Y axis represents −2 to +2). The main program first reads from the user the number of harmonic components to use, sets the video mode, clears the screen and then calls a function which draws the axes of the graph. Next a function which plots each component on the graph is called; this will produce the display shown in Figure 15.7 for 4 components.

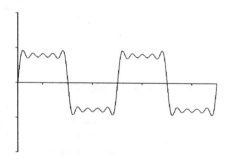

Figure 15.8 Result of Fourier composition

The screen is then cleared and the axes are redrawn. A function is then called, which plots the resultant (i.e. sum) of the components and produces a graph (for 4 components), as shown in Figure 15.8.

The *drawaxes()* function is simple and draws two lines from the programmer's origin of lengths determined by the predefined axis length values. An added feature is that small lines are also drawn along the axes to represent scale marks. The *draw_components* function is as follows:

```
void draw_components(int c)
    {
    int harmn,x,y,oldx,oldy,n;
    double angle,amp;

    for (n=1;n<=c;n++)
    {
      harmn=n*2-1;
      _setcolor(n%15+1);
      oldx=0; oldy=0;

      for (x=0;x<=X_AXIS;x++)
      {
        angle=X_FULL_SCALE*x/X_AXIS;
        angle=angle/180*PI;

        amp=(1.0/harmn)*sin(angle*harmn);
        y=amp*Y_AXIS/Y_FULL_SCALE;

        myline(oldx,oldy,x,y);
        oldx=x; oldy=y;
      }
    }
}
```

The parameter *c* indicates how many components to draw and controls a loop which draws one component on each iteration. At the start of each iteration, it is necessary to calculate which harmonic is being drawn. This is done using the statement:

```
harmn=n*2-1;
```

which gives the values of the odd harmonics (1,3,5,7 etc.) as the loop continues and *n* is incremented. Then a selection occurs of a colour for the trace to be drawn. With 16 colours available (with indexes from 0 to 15), we calculate a number in the range 1 to 15, based on the value of *n*. Therefore, each harmonic will be a different colour. The colour index 0 is avoided here, because it is the index for black which will not show up.

We now start to plot the graph. This involves stepping along the 500 pixel positions on the X axis and for each one calculating the value of the corresponding Y pixel and plotting this point. We therefore have a loop which steps along the X axis. For each position along the axis, we must then calculate what angle this corresponds to (remember that the X axis represents 0° to 720°).

This is done with the following statements:

```
angle=X_FULL_SCALE*x/X_AXIS;
angle=angle/180*PI;
```

Notice that the *sin* function also requires the angle to be converted to radians, which is done by the second statement. It is now possible to calculate the amplitude of the harmonic at this angle, using the statement:

```
amp=(1.0/harmn)*sin(angle*harmn);
```

This gives a value between ± 1, which must now be converted to a number of pixels up or down the Y axis. This is done by the following statement:

```
y=amp*Y_AXIS/Y_FULL_SCALE;
```

This now fixes a point on the graph. We could now simply use a plot function to set the pixel at this position. However, this may cause the graph to have large gaps in it if Y is changing quickly. Instead, a straight line is drawn from the last point plotted to the new one just calculated. This results in a much better quality of drawing. The variables *oldx* and *oldy* are used to store the coordinates of the last point plotted.

The function to draw the resultant is similar to the function just described, but is complicated by the need to perform the summation for each point plotted. The complete program is as follows:

```
/* Demonstrates composition of a square wave */
/* from sinusoids using the principles       */
/* described by Fourier                       */

#include <stdio.h>
#include <conio.h>
#include <graph.h>
#include <math.h>

#define PI 3.1415926    /* Value of Pi */

/* Defined origin of user coordinates */
/* on screen                          */
#define X_ORIGIN 100
#define Y_ORIGIN 240

/* Define lengths of axes in pixels   */
#define X_AXIS    500
#define Y_AXIS    200

/* define maximum scale reading of axes   */
/* ie x-axis represents 0 to 720 degrees */
```

```
/* and Y represents values from 0 to +-2 */
#define X_FULL_SCALE 720.0
#define Y_FULL_SCALE 2.0

/* define how many scale marks an axes */
#define X_MARKS       8
#define Y_MARKS       2

/* Function Prototypes */
void drawaxes(void);
void myline(int x1, int y1, int x2, int y2);
void draw_components(int c);
void draw_resultant(int c);

/***********************************************/
main()
{
  int components;

  printf("\nFourier composition demo program");
  printf("\nHow many components to use?");
  scanf("%i",&components);

  _setvideomode(_VRES16COLOR);

  /* Draw the individual components */
  _clearscreen(_GCLEARSCREEN);
  drawaxes();
  draw_components(components);

  /* Draw result of adding each component */
  _clearscreen(_GCLEARSCREEN);
  drawaxes();
  draw_resultant(components);

  getchar();
  _setvideomode(_DEFAULTMODE);
}
/***********************************************/
void drawaxes(void)
{
  int coord,n;

  _setcolor(15);   /* Draw in white */

  /* X axis */
  myline(0,0,X_AXIS,0);

  /* draw marks along X axis */
  for (n=0;n<=X_MARKS;n++)
  {
    coord=n*X_AXIS/X_MARKS;
```

```
    myline (coord, 0, coord, -5);
  }

  /* Y axis */
  myline (0, -Y_AXIS, 0, Y_AXIS);

  /* draw marks along Y axis */
  for (n=-X_MARKS;n<=X_MARKS;n++)
  {
    coord=n*Y_AXIS/Y_MARKS;
    myline (0, coord, -5, coord);
  }
}
/*************************************************/
void draw_components(int c)
{
  int harmn,x,y,oldx,oldy,n;
  double angle,amp;

  /* Loop for required number of components */
  for (n=1;n<=c;n++)
  {
    /* Calculate harmonic ie. 1,3,5,7... */
    harmn=n*2-1;

    /* select new colour for this harmonic */
    _setcolor (n%15+1);

    oldx=0; oldy=0;

    /* Loop for each point along X axis */
    for (x=0;x<=X_AXIS;x++)
      {
      /* Calculate angle which corresponds to */
      /* this point on X axis. Convert to rads*/
      angle=X_FULL_SCALE*x/X_AXIS;
      angle=angle/180*PI;

      /* Calculate amplitude of harmonic */
      amp= (1.0/harmn) *sin (angle*harmn);

      /* Convert value of amp to distance */
      /* up Y axis in pixels               */
      y=amp*Y_AXIS/Y_FULL_SCALE;

      /* Draw line from last point to new */
      /* point using mapped line function */
      myline (oldx, oldy, x, y);
      oldx=x; oldy=y;
    }
  }
}
```

```
/*************************************************/
void draw_resultant(int c)
{
  int harmn,x,y,oldx,oldy,n;
  double angle,sum;

  _setcolor(10);
  oldx=0; oldy=0;

  /* Loop for each point on the X axis */
  for (x=0;x<=X_AXIS;x++)
  {
    /*Calculate angle at this position on axis*/
    angle=X_FULL_SCALE*x/X_AXIS;
    angle=angle/180*PI;
    sum=0;

    /* Loop for each harmonic */
    for (harmn=1;harmn/2<=c;harmn=harmn+2)
    {
      sum=sum+(1.0/harmn)*sin(angle*harmn);
    }
    /* Sum of harmonics now converted to */
    /* distance up Y axis in pixels      */
    y=sum*Y_AXIS/Y_FULL_SCALE;

    myline(oldx,oldy,x,y);
    oldx=x; oldy=y;
  }
}

/*************************************************/
/* Draws line using logical coordinates       */
void myline(int x1,int y1,int x2,int y2)
{
  _moveto(x1+X_ORIGIN,Y_ORIGIN-y1);
  _lineto(x2+X_ORIGIN,Y_ORIGIN-y2);
}
```

15.7 Summary

- Most modern personal computers have specialist hardware to drive the display. These adapters often allow different modes of operation that offer a selection of resolutions and colour palettes.

- There is often a text mode in which the display hardware is dedicated to the display of text. There are often library routines to manipulate such displays, such as moving the cursor to specific locations.

- In graphics mode most displays offer resolutions of several hundred pixels both down and across the screen. These have associated coordinates, such that any point on the screen can be referenced.

- The most basic graphic function is to plot a pixel. Using this, functions for drawing lines, circles or any other shape, can be implemented.

- It is often awkward to use the physical coordinate system of the screen when programming. Therefore, the concept of mapping can be used to produce graphical functions which are easier to use.

- There is no standard defined for graphical functions in C. Therefore, each C implementation may be different. However, most share the same basic functions, although their precise usage and names may vary.

15.8   Exercises

1) Write a function to make the machine act as a simple digital clock so that it displays the time in the format HH:MM:SS in the centre of the screen. This time should be updated every second and flickering should be kept to a minimum. Use twenty-four hour format and leading zero should be inserted. If the machine has a text mode for the display, then this should be used in conjunction with a *settextposition* type function and *printf*.

2) Produce an animated analogue clock face as shown below, using graphics functions. This should have moving hands and flickering should be kept to a minimum. There is a lot of fiddling required to get a good quality display.

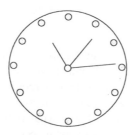

3) Write a program to plot the phase response of a simple RC low-pass filter with cutoff frequency of 1 kHz. Note that the X axis will be logarithmic.

16 Software Engineering

16.1 Introduction

Writing programs, which is what we have been doing so far, is only one aspect of software engineering and there are many other important aspects to the production of quality software which we have not looked at in any detail. These include the identification of requirements, specification, design method, testing and maintenance. Software engineering is a huge area for us to try and cover here. All we can attempt to do in these few pages is to illustrate some of the important aspects of which the reader should be aware and show how they can be applied in a simple manner to our programs. We will also examine some of the features of C which help in the production of large and complex programs.

16.2 Software life-cycle

A piece of software, when it is developed, goes through a number of stages before and after delivery to a user. A simple example of such a life-cycle is shown in Figure 16.1.

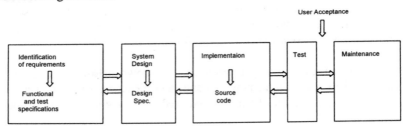

Figure 16.1 Software life-cycle

The first stage is to identify carefully what is actually required. It is obviously bad practice to implement a system which works, but does not solve the original problem. It is therefore vital that the precise requirements are understood and are written down in detail in the form of a functional specification. It is often the case that the user does not quite know what is required and so this stage can involve lengthy discussion. The functional specification is eventually agreed by user and software producer and can then be passed on to the team who will design the system. It should also be possible at this stage to write a test specification from the functional specification, to ensure that the final system will meet the original requirements.

The next stage is design. This involves breaking the problem down into manageable pieces and deciding on a strategy for implementing the system. The result of this will be a design specification that details the function of the different parts of the system and how they should interact. This specification can then be used for the implementation stage, where the actual source code is written. The implementation stage is typically quite short, since most of the difficult design work has already been done.

The resulting system must then be tested against the test specification and when the system is shown to be satisfactory, it can be shipped to the customer for use.

Any useful software will probably need modification during its lifetime. Therefore, a major part of its life-cycle is maintenance while in use. This involves fixing errors previously undetected, or modifying the system to satisfy the user's changing requirements.

Notice that all stages in the life-cycle are reiterative. It is unlikely that the initial requirements will be exactly correct, but likely that flaws in the design stage will be found during implementation. Therefore, much back-tracking and review of each stage will occur.

Most of what has been said applies to the production of large systems, which may require tens or hundreds of man-years to produce. However, we should continue to apply these principles to the simple programs that we have produced.

16.3 Indentifying requirements

Many of the programs you will be required to write will be exercises where the specification is already carefully written. However, it is often the case that there are ambiguities or omissions which will need clarification. In the case where a specification needs to be produced, it is well worth the effort of formally stating the requirements, as this requires a thorough understanding of the problem before proceeding.

In general, a functional specification consists of the inputs to a system (e.g. this program expects a list of 100 real numbers between 0 and 1000) and a description of how this input is processed. Details of the output are also required (e.g. the output will be a list of 50 integer numbers in a file called 'output.dat'). Other items to mention are how the program copes with exceptions (i.e. unexpected inputs). For example, how does a program react when a real number is entered, but an integer is expected?

16.4 System design

There are numerous ways of going about designing the system, but we will concentrate on the general principles of top-down and bottom-up design. The objective of system design is to split a problem up into manageable pieces and then define exactly what each component should do and how it interacts with the rest of the system.

We have already seen examples of splitting up problems into manageable pieces. Many of the programs we have seen use a collection of different functions, each with a small, well-defined task to perform. The complete system is then produced by calling these functions up as appropriate. Therefore, for our programs the design phase will consist of indentifying what functions we will require, carefully defining their operation, and then stating how they will interact with other parts of the system (e.g. what arguments they require, which global variables they will modify, what they will return).

We can take two approaches to this problem. For example, consider a graphics program to produce pie charts. We could legitimately start by producing all the basic graphical functions that we will require (i.e. write specifications for line drawing function, arc function, area fill function, character drawing function). With these now defined, we could then define a hierarchically higher set of functions to draw a pie slice or a string of text. Above this, another hierarchy of functions could be defined, to draw complete pie charts with annotations, as shown in Figure 16.2.

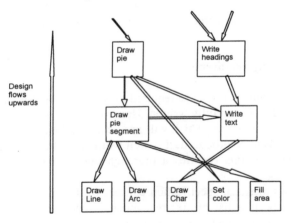

Figure 16.2 Bottom-up design

A different approach would be to assume initially the existence of the lower functions, and start at the top of the design by writing the master functions. These definitions will then make reference to hierarchically lower functions which will then need to be defined. This approach is called top-down design. The choice of which approach to use depends on the particular situation, or even on personal preference.

A description of each function should be produced detailing the number, order and types of arguments, then the return type (if any), and a note of any global variables that it uses or modifies. A description of what the function does is also required, along with how it behaves when exceptions occur (i.e. how does a square root function behave if the argument is negative).

This can all be collected into a total description of the system, called a design specification. Note the difference between a functional and or design specification; one is a description of what the system will do, and the other is a description of how it will do it.

16.5 Implementation

This should be a fairly trivial task if the design stage has been undertaken properly. Each function is written, compiled and debugged. Where possible, testing should be performed as each new section is completed. If using a bottom-up approach, each level of the hierarchy can be coded, and then specially written test functions can be used to drive the new code to verify its operation. When using top-down approaches, it may therefore be necessary to write simple dummy functions that emulate the non-existent lower hierarchies, in order to test the existing code.

16.6 Testing

This is probably the area most overlooked by novice programmers. Testing of software can mean many things. We have already said in the last section that each individual function should be tested, if possible, as the system is produced. Then, as the levels of hierarchy are produced, the partially complete sections of the system can be tested. This is commonly called integration testing. This is all performed during implementation with reference to the design specification. However, when the system is complete we must then perform another type of test.

The completed system must now be thoroughly tested to ensure that it meets the original requirements (a process usually called validation) and that it is reliable. For our types of simple programs, validation will probably mean re-reading the original functional specification and trying some inputs for which we know the expected results. In commercial situations, the validation process can be very much more rigorous and formalised.

Reliability is also something we should consider here. Our programs should be robust, so that slapping a hand across the keyboard will not make it crash. Also, our programs should be capable of behaving sensibly when they run into problems (e.g. it cannot find the roots of a quadratic, because they are complex). Also, our programs should be immune to the problems of arithmetic overflows, or writing over the ends of arrays (very common problems with C programs). Therefore, always thoroughly test programs. This may mean sitting down and running a program repeatedly with different inputs and trying ridiculous inputs to see what happens. Also, try inputs at the limits of any known ranges, and unusual values, which may cause problems (e.g. zero or an empty string).

Hopefully, after some modifications, the system should appear satisfactory and can be put to use. In a commercial situation, test results would be seen and analysed by the customer before acceptance.

16.7   Documentation and maintenance

Any useful piece of software will presumably have a long life time and will be re-issued with improvements and fixes to known bugs. This forms the maintenance phase of the life-cycle and can run into many years. Consequently, the people performing the maintenance may not be the original team who designed the system. Therefore, it is absolutely vital that documentation is produced, enabling subsequent engineers to understand the system. Such documentation will consist of the original specifications, listings, testing procedures and records of modifications. In addition, other documentation will usually need to be produced for the benefit of the users, so that they are able to drive and administer the system.

It is common for programmers to loathe the idea of carefully documenting everything, but given the complexity of modern software systems, it is a vital activity.

16.8   Software engineering using C

We are concerned with writing useful, reliable programs in C. The reader should now be in a position to produce relatively complex and large systems, using their knowledge of the language and the guidelines set out in this chapter. However, so far all the programs we have looked at have still been small enough for a single person to write and understand. We will continue by looking at a feature of C (which is also found in other languages) necessary for when programs become too large for one person to manage effectively. This will also lead us on to a better understanding of how the libraries supplied with C compilers are organised.

16.9   Separate file compilation

When several people are working on a project, they cannot all work on the same file. Therefore, it is necessary to break the program into separate files which can be individually edited and compiled. Therefore, the final system can be built up from the contribution of many such files.

All our programs to date have been created inside a single file (or compilation unit), thus keeping things simple. If we were to split up one of our programs such that some of the functions were in one file, and others in another file, then it is unlikely that either file would compile individually. This is because each file would contain references to functions in the other file and, since the compiler only works on single files, it would be ignorant of the existence of these functions. We therefore need a mechanism to allow information to be shared between source files.

For illustration, we will consider the example of section 15.6, in which we use a number of our own graphical primitives (such as drawing lines) to plot a graph which shows how a square wave is composed of a number of sinusoids. A useful feature would be to have all the graphical primitives in a file separate from the functions concerned with drawing the graph. This would allow us to reuse the graphical primitives for other programs, since they would exist separately. Therefore, we might have a file called *myprims.c,* as follows:

```
/* Defs. of mapped graphical primitive functions */

#include <graph.h>   /* Header for graphics lib. */
#include "myprim.h" /* header file in local dir. */

/* Draw line relative to selected origin */
void myline(int x1, int y1, int x2, int y2)
{
  _moveto(x1+X_ORIGIN, Y_ORIGIN-y1);
  _lineto(x2+X_ORIGIN, Y_ORIGIN-y2);
}

/* Draw circle relative to selected origin */
void mycircle(int x, int y, int r)
{
  ellipse(x+CENTRE_X+r, CENTRE_Y-y+r, x+CENTRE_X-r,
          CENTRE_Y-y-r);
}
            .
            .

/* Fill area */
void myfill(int x, int y, int c)
{
  fillarea(x+CENTRE_X,CENTRE_Y-y,c);
}
```

These functions are exactly as described in chapter 15, but as it stands this file cannot be compiled because there are references to constants, such as *CENTRE_X*, that are missing. These could be entered into this file directly, using

#*define* directives, but if this was done then functions in other files would not have access to these constants should they be required. We therefore place these definitions into a header file called *myprims.h* which we then include inside the source code file. The header file will therefore appear as follows:

```
/* Definition of new origin position on screen */
#define CENTRE_X  320       /* X origin */
#define CENTRE_Y  240       /* Y origin */
```

This header is then included in our source code file, using the line:

```
#include "myprims.h"
```

Note that we have used quotes here instead of the <..> symbols. Previously, all the header files we have used have been those supplied with the libraries that come with the compiler. The <..> symbols indicate that the compiler should look to the area where such header files are kept to find the specified file. If the filename is in quotes, the compiler will look to the current directory in which it is working. We must therefore ensure that the compiler can find our new header file in the current directory. It should now be possible to compile the *myprims.c* file, resulting in an object code file called *myprims.obj*, or similar.

We then can write the program to draw the appropriate graphs in a new file called *fourier.c*, with reference to our graphical functions, without actually rewriting the function definitions in this file. The file will appear as follows:

```
/* Demonstrates the composition of a square wave */
/* from sinusoids as described by fourier        */
#include <stdio.h>
        .
        .
main()
{
        .
        .
}
void drawaxes(void)
{
  int coord,n;

  _setcolor(15);
  myline(0,0,X_AXIS,0);
        .
        .
}
```

The important point to note is the reference to *myline*, which is a function now defined in another file. The compiler will accept that the function is defined elsewhere, provided that it can check that the function call has the correct number of arguments, each of the right type, and that the return type is correct. However, since the compiler knows nothing about this function, a function prototype must be provided, so that the compiler can perform these checks. We could therefore just provide the function prototype, as we have done before at the start of this source file. However, this is not good since it does not necessarily mean that the function call and prototype in this file which might match are actually the same as the function definition in the file *myprims.c*. Ideally, we need to compare the function prototype with the call and the actual definition. This is achieved by placing the prototypes of the functions defined in *myprim.c* in the header *myprim.h*. The header file *myprims.h* will therefore appear as follows:

```
/* Definition of new origin position on screen */
#define CENTRE_X  320        /* X origin */
#define CENTRE_Y  240        /* Y origin */

/* Function prototypes of graphical primitives */
void myline(int x1, int y1, int x2, int y2);
void mycircle(int x, int y, int r);
        .
        .
void myfill(int x, int y, int c);
```

If this file is included in both *myprims.c* and *fourier.c* when they are compiled, then all calls and definitions of the functions are compared with these prototypes, and errors are flagged if differences are detected.

The final stage of producing the executable code is to link the two separate object files, along with any standard library functions required, to produce a single executable file, as shown in Figure 16.3.

Note that all the standard library files provided are used in the same way as just described. Each library is a compiled set of functions and the linker can extract from the object files any function that it requires for the final executable code. The original source code for these libraries is often not supplied, but the function prototypes required for us to use these functions are available in the header files with which we are familiar (e.g. *stdio.h* for prototypes of *printf* and *scanf*).

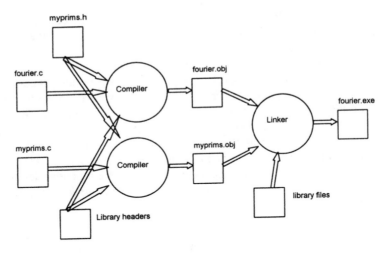

Figure 16.3 Multiple file compilation

16.10   Make files

When producing a system with a large number of contributing files, it can be laborious to list these each time a complete compile or link of the system is performed. Consequently, most C systems provide a make-file facility, so that a file can be produced which lists the names of all the contributing files. The compiler and linker can then automatically read this list and process all the files that it contains. This saves time and reduces errors.

16.11   Summary

- Software engineering is a term applied to all aspects of the production of quality software.

- Although software engineering techniques for commercial use are complex and well developed, the general principles can still be applied to improve the quality of small programs.

- C provides facilities for separate file compilations making the production of large programs much simpler. This facility is dependent on the use of header files for sharing information between many source code files.

Appendix A Glossary

Argument A value that is passed to a function.

Assembler A software tool which converts assembly language programs into machine code.

Binary Representation of values as sequences of 1's and 0's.

Bit Binary digit. Basic unit used to represent data and programs in a computer. A bit can assume values of 1 or 0 only.

Bitwise A type of operator used to manipulate the bits of an integer.

Byte A group of 8 bits. A byte can assume 2^8 possible bit patterns (256), which can be used to represent numbers, character codes or program codes.

Buffer An area of memory used for communication between programs and I/O devices. A buffer allows input data to arrive before a program is ready to process it, or stores output data to be sent to a device.

Character A printable symbol (usually alphanumeric or punctuation) which is represented as an 8-bit binary code. The assignment of codes to characters is standardised and called the ASCII code. Some character codes do not represent symbols but are used to control the printer or monitor to which they are sent (e.g. carriage return).

Compiler Software tool which converts high-level language source code into object code.

Crash A malfunction of a computer. Often caused by the code in memory which is being executed becoming corrupted. Often the result is that the machine 'freezes' and will not respond. Usually the machine will need to be reset.

Cursor A position on the screen at which the next textual or graphic output will be placed. The cursor position is often marked with a flashing symbol.

Declaration A statement of an association between an identifier and the attributes of a variable, function or type. Note that a declaration does not cause memory to be set aside for storage, it simply associates a name with some other object.

Definition Creation (and possibly initialisation) of a variable by reserving storage space in memory with an associated identifier. Also the association of an identifier with a section of code (i.e. a function definition). Note that a definition always results in memory being set aside for data or code. A type is also associated with the defined object.

Directive   An instruction to the preprocessor to perform some operation on the source code before compilation.

Escape sequence   A combination of a backslash (\) followed by a letter or digits which represents control characters in characters strings and constants.

Executable code   See Machine code.

Format string   A string used in *scanf* or *printf* to specify the format of input and output. Usually consists of a character string containing format specifiers and other characters.

Format specifier   A description of how *scanf* and *printf* will manipulate values which are input and output. Also implies the type of representation used for storage of the values. Uses the symbol %.

FILE pointer   A pointer to a structure which contains information on an open file. Its value is used by library functions which manipulate files.

Function   A set of statements and declarations with an associated identifier which can be executed simply by quoting its identifier elsewhere.

Global   A variable defined such that it can be referenced from any area of the source file.

Header file   A source file which contains commonly used definitions and declarations which can be inserted into a source file.

Hexadecimal   Base 16 number system. The letters A to F are used to represent the extra 6 numerals required.

Identifier   A name which is associated with a function, variable or type.

Indirection   Accessing data through a pointer, rather than directly.

Interface   A hardware device allowing the CPU to communicate with peripheral devices.

Library   A file containing compiled function which may be incorporated with user-created code by the linker to form the final executable code.

Linker   Software tool which produces executable code from contributing object code files.

Local   A variable which can only be referenced within the function, or block, in which it is defined.

Machine code   Form of program which can be executed directly by the CPU. Stored in memory as a sequence of binary codes.

Member   One of the component variables which form a record.

Memory   Usually taken to mean part of computer hardware used for storage of programs and data. Consists of many millions of electronic switches to represent bits. Usually organised into byte structure.

Object code
Output of a compiler. Consists of partially complete machine code, which is not fixed at any memory address and may make references to items in other object code files.

Octal
Base 8 number system. Digits 0 to 7 used.

Operand
An expression which is the subject of an operator.

Operator
A symbol which specifies how the operand (for unary operators) or operands (for binary operators) are manipulated within an expression.

Operating system
A program which manages a computer. It allows user programs to be loaded into memory and run, as well as providing I/O and other services to programs.

Parameter
A variable which receives a value passed to a function.

Pointer
A variable which contains the memory address of another variable, function or constant.

Port
Communication channel to an external device via an interface.

Preprocessor
A tool which manipulates source code prior to compilation.

Prototype
A declaration which includes the name, return type and parameters of a function defined elsewhere in the program.

Structure
A set of variables of different types which are grouped together under one name. Each variable contained in the structure is called a member.

Scope
The areas of the source code in which a variable (or other named item) can be referenced.

String
A sequence of characters. Often stored in a character array or quoted in programs using double quote marks (""). The ends of strings are usually marked with a null character (\0).

Source code
Original program code. In the case of the C language this is the C statements entered by the programmer into a file.

Tag
A name (identifier) which identifies a member of a record.

Type
An attribute of a value which determines how it is stored in memory.

Type casting
An operation where a value of one type is converted to another type.

Variable
A space in memory set aside for the storage of values. Variables are usually given a name (identifier).

Appendix B ASCII codes

The following table lists all 128 defined ASCII codes. The first column represents the codes in decimal, the second column represents the code in hexadecimal, the third column is the corresponding character or control character mnemonic, and the final column describes some of the control characters functions, or gives the name of some of the more obscure characters.

The non-printable characters, called control characters, all have defined meanings indicated by a two- or three-letter mnemonic. Many of these do not concern us, but the more important ones are described below.

When writing programs in C we must sometimes use escape sequences starting with the \ symbol to write a character. The escape sequences that are defined for certain characters are shown. Note that the \n code does not appear below since it actually represents two characters, the line feed character which moves the print position vertically down one line and then a carriage return to move to the start of the line.

Note that the ASCII set requires only seven bits to encode all the defined characters. Since most machines use a byte which is eight bits to store character codes, the remaining 128 codes are often used for additional characters. However, these additional characters will differ from machine to machine.

0	0	NUL	(String terminator \0)	23	17	ETB	
1	1	SOH		24	18	CAN	
2	2	STX		25	19	EM	
3	3	ETX		26	1a	SUB	
4	4	EOT		27	1b	ESC	
5	5	ENQ		28	1c	FS	
6	6	ACK		29	1d	GS	
7	7	BEL	(Sounds bell \a)	30	1e	RS	
8	8	BS	(Backspace \b)	31	1f	US	
9	9	HT	(Horizontal tab \t)	32	20		(Space)
10	a	LF	(line feed)	33	21	!	(Exclamation)
11	b	VT	(Vertical tab \v)	34	22	"	(Double quote \")
12	c	FF	(form feed \f)	35	23	#	(Hash)
13	d	CR	(Carriage return \r)	36	24	$	(Dollar)
14	e	SO		37	25	%	(Percent)
15	f	SI		38	26	&	(Ampersand)
16	10	DLE		39	27	'	(Single quote \')
17	11	DC1		40	28	(	(Left parenthesis)
18	12	DC2		41	29	)	(Right parenthesis)
19	13	DC3		42	2a	*	(Asterisk)
20	14	DC4		43	2b	+	(Plus)
21	15	NAK		44	2c	,	(Comma)
22	16	SYN		45	2d	-	(Hyphen, minus)

46	2e	.	(Full stop, Dec.point)
47	2f	/	(Slash, oblique)
48	30	0	
49	31	1	
50	32	2	
51	33	3	
52	34	4	
53	35	5	
54	36	6	
55	37	7	
56	38	8	
57	39	9	
58	3a	:	(Colon)
59	3b	;	(Semicolon)
60	3c	<	(Greater than)
61	3d	=	(Equal)
62	3e	>	(Less than)
63	3f	?	(Question mark)
64	40	@	(At)
65	41	A	
66	42	B	
67	43	C	
68	44	D	
69	45	E	
70	46	F	
71	47	G	
72	48	H	
73	49	I	
74	4a	J	
75	4b	K	
76	4c	L	
77	4d	M	
78	4e	N	
79	4f	O	
80	50	P	
81	51	Q	
82	52	R	
83	53	S	
84	54	T	
85	55	U	
86	56	V	
87	57	W	
88	58	X	
89	59	Y	
90	5a	Z	
91	5b	[	(Left bracket)
92	5c	\	(Backslash ||)
93	5d	]	(Right bracket)

94	5e	^	(Accent, Circumflex)
95	5f	_	(Underscore)
96	60	`	(Opening quote)
97	61	a	
98	62	b	
99	63	c	
100	64	d	
101	65	e	
102	66	f	
103	67	g	
104	68	h	
105	69	i	
106	6a	j	
107	6b	k	
108	6c	l	
109	6d	m	
110	6e	n	
111	6f	o	
112	70	p	
113	71	q	
114	72	r	
115	73	s	
116	74	t	
117	75	u	
118	76	v	
119	77	w	
120	78	x	
121	79	y	
122	7a	z	
123	7b	{	(Left brace)
124	7c	|	(Vertical bar)
125	7d	}	(Right brace)
126	7e	~	(Tilde)
127	7f	DEL	

Appendix C Errors in C

This appendix is a quick guide to the most common errors that befall novice programmers. A quick flick through this may help save a lot of time when you get compilation, linking or run-time errors. It is by no means comprehensive, but covers the majority of the initial types of problems that you might encounter.

Error messages vary between compilers, but the generalised messages below should help to identify the sources of error.

1) Syntax errors

These are errors in the program code detected by the compiler. They are caused when the rules governing the structure of the language are violated. They are usually easily remedied by a simple edit and then the program can be recompiled.

Missing ';' A very common error. May not be noticed by the compiler until the next statement is reached and so may apply to statement before the one where the compiler flags an error.

End of file found or unexpected. Another common error which is caused by not closing all curly brackets (i.e. there are '}' symbols missing). Proper indentation should eliminate this. Can also be caused by not closing a comment and so a whole section to the end of the file is commented out. Look for unclosed '/*' symbol which may be high up the file. Also, check that all *do*'s have corresponding *while*'s.

Cannot open include file. Caused by an error in the name of the include file or by trying to use a non-existent one. Most include files end in '*.h*' and are contained between < ... >.

Newline in constant or string. This means that you have started a string with double quotes, but have not closed the quotes. Common in *printf* and *scanf* statements where format string is not closed.

Different levels of indirection. Caused by using double quotes in the place of single quotes, or vice versa. Use single quotes for single characters and double quotes for a string of characters. Also occurs when a pointer variable is incorrectly used.

2) Semantic errors

These are caused when the program structure is correct but the meaning does not make sense. An example might be to call a function which does not exist. Even though the function call may be syntactically correct, the compiler or linker cannot complete their tasks.

Undefined identifier. This is caused when you use a variable name, function name or other identifier which is not defined. Define the required variable/ function or check spelling/case. In programs with user functions, check scope of variable and that it is defined locally to the area where it is being referenced, or it is globally defined.

No function prototype given. This is a common warning and is usually caused by failing to include the correct header file when using library functions. Check documentation for appropriate file required for the function. Also check spelling/case of the function name. Because it is usually a warning the program might still run correctly. If the error is caused by a programmer-defined function, check that a function prototype exists and has the correct name.

Unresolved external. This linker error might accompany the previous error. It is caused by trying to use a non-existent function. Check spelling/case.

3) Run-time errors

These are errors in the way the program is written, allowing something to go wrong as the program is running. A common example is when the program has to calculate a negative square root, or divide by zero. The error occurs on the output screen as the program is running.

Divide by zero. The program attempted a divide by zero. Re-think how the program works.

sqrt — **Domain error.** Caused by trying to find the square root of a negative number. The program may continue running after this error.

Stack overflow. Caused by having large local variables in functions, or by continuous recursion (i.e. a function keeps calling itself). The linker usually has an option for increasing stack size.

4) Bugs

These are not errors which the C environment will detect. The program will run, but not do the job that was intended. It is the programmer who is at fault, since the code is incorrect for the problem. Usually, a look through the program or single stepping will reveal the problems. However, here are a few nasty little things to watch out for:

if statement always executes

```
if (x>0) ;
{
  printf("Hello");
}
```

This section will always print 'Hello' even if x is less than zero. This is because of the semicolon after $(x>0)$. This indicates the end of the *if* statement. The program then continues and executes the next statement (*printf*) regardless of the value of x. Removing the semicolon means that the code between curly brackets comes part of the *if* statement and then works as expected.

if statement executes when it shouldn't or doesn't when it should

```
x=9;
if (x=4)
{
  printf("%i",x);
}
```

This would appear not to print anything. In fact it prints the value 4! The reason is that we have used '=' instead of '==' in the test. A single equals is an assignment (i.e. $x=4$ means x becomes equal to 4). A double equals is a test (i.e. $x==4$ means is x equal to 4). Since we are using the wrong one in the *if* then x is set to 4. The *if* statement also interprets this as a 'true' value and executes the *printf*.

for loop only executes once

```
for (n=1;n<=10;n++) ;
{
  printf("%i",n);
}
```

This would appear to print all the numbers from 1 to 10. Instead it just prints eleven. The reason is the semicolon at the end of the line beginning *for*. This semicolon marks the end of the loop, so the program then executes nothing ten times leaving *n* set to eleven and then carries on after the loop passing the *printf* once. Removing the semicolon will mean that everything between the brackets becomes included in the loop.

scanf doesn't work

Lots to go wrong here. First check that you have put a '&' before each variable. If it still does not work, then check the types of the variables against the format string codes (e.g. %i for an integer, %lf for a long float (double), %c for a character). If it still does not work, ensure that the format string contains nothing but format codes separated by spaces (e.g. "%i,%f" should be "%i %f").

printf prints values incorrectly

If you have ascertained by single stepping that *printf* is not printing correctly then check the variable types against the format codes (i.e. use %li for a long integer, %f for a float, %c for a character and %s for a string).

Variables change values when they shouldn't

Check conditional statements which test for equality use '==' and not '='. For example:

```
while (x=9)
```

should be

```
while (x==9)
```

Appendix D Keywords

The following list contains words with predefined meaning in C programs. Consequently, these words cannot be used for other purposes such as variable or function identifiers. All keywords use lower case characters. Note that certain compilers may have extra non-standard keywords available.

auto	break	case	char
const	continue	default	do
double	else	enum	extern
float	for	goto	if
int	long	register	return
short	signed	sizeof	static
struct	switch	typedef	union
unsigned	void	volatile	while

Other words are also predefined in C which are concerned with the standard libraries (such as *printf*). These are defined in the standard header files used in conjunction with the libraries. If a header file is not included, then these identifiers can be used for other purposes, but this is usually best avoided.

Index